Stanley in India

Sept 1949.

The Design of Experiments

The
Design of Experiments

By

Ronald A. Fisher, Sc.D., F.R.S.

Arthur Balfour Professor of Genetics, University of Cambridge
Honorary Member, American Statistical Association and
American Academy of Arts and Sciences, formerly
Galton Professor, University of London
Foreign Member of the Royal
Swedish Academy of
Sciences

FIFTH EDITION

Oliver and Boyd
Edinburgh: Tweeddale Court
London: 98 Great Russell Street, W.C.
1949

FIRST PUBLISHED . . 1935
SECOND EDITION . . 1937
THIRD EDITION . . . 1942
FOURTH EDITION . . 1947
FIFTH EDITION . . . 1949

PRINTED AND PUBLISHED IN GREAT BRITAIN
BY OLIVER AND BOYD LTD., EDINBURGH

PREFACE TO FIRST EDITION

IN 1925 the author wrote a book (*Statistical Methods for Research Workers*) with the object of supplying practical experimenters and, incidentally, teachers of mathematical statistics, with a connected account of the applications in laboratory work of some of the more recent advances in statistical theory. Some of the new methods, such as the analysis of variance, were found to be so intimately related with problems of experimental design that a considerable part of the eighth chapter was devoted to the technique of agricultural experimentation, and these sections have been progressively enlarged with subsequent editions, in response to frequent requests for a fuller treatment of the subject. The design of experiments is, however, too large a subject, and of too great importance to the general body of scientific workers, for any incidental treatment to be adequate. A clear grasp of simple and standardised statistical procedures will, as the reader may satisfy himself, go far to elucidate the principles of experimentation; but these procedures are themselves only the means to a more important end. Their part is to satisfy the requirements of sound and intelligible experimental design, and to supply the machinery for unambiguous interpretation. To attain a clear grasp of these requirements we need to study designs which have been widely successful in many fields, and to examine their structure in relation to the requirements of valid inference.

The examples chosen in this book are aimed at

illustrating the principles of successful experimentation ; first, in their simplest possible applications, and later, in regard to the more elaborate structures by which the different advantages sought may be combined. Statistical discussion has been reduced to a minimum, and all the processes required will be found more fully exemplified in the previous work. The reader is, however, advised that the detailed working of numerical examples is essential to a thorough grasp, not only of the technique, but of the principles by which an experimental procedure may be judged to be satisfactory and effective.

GALTON LABORATORY
July 1935

PREFACE TO FIFTH EDITION

THE second edition differed little from the first, published a year earlier. Apart from numerical corrections the principal changes were the fuller treatment of completely orthogonal squares in Section 35, and the addition of examples in Section 47·1, representing some of the newly developed combinatorial arrangements, which are attracting considerable interest. In the third edition Sections 45·1 and 45·2 were added, giving a more comprehensive view of the possibilities of confounding with many factors, and introducing the method of double confounding. In the fourth edition, Section 62·1 has been added on the fiducial limits of a ratio. In the fifth edition, Section 35·01 on configuration in three or more dimensions has been added. The numbers of sections have not been changed.

DEPARTMENT OF GENETICS, CAMBRIDGE
1948

CONTENTS

I. INTRODUCTION

PAGE

1. The Grounds on which Evidence is Disputed I
2. The Mathematical Attitude towards Induction . . . 3
3. The Rejection of Inverse Probability 6
4. The Logic of the Laboratory 7

II. THE PRINCIPLES OF EXPERIMENTATION, ILLUSTRATED BY A PSYCHO-PHYSICAL EXPERIMENT

5. Statement of Experiment 11
6. Interpretation and its Reasoned Basis 12
7. The Test of Significance 13
8. The Null Hypothesis 15
9. Randomisation ; the Physical Basis of the Validity of the Test . 17
10. The Effectiveness of Randomisation 19
11. The Sensitiveness of an Experiment. Effects of Enlargement and Repetition 21
12. Qualitative Methods of increasing Sensitiveness . . . 22

III. A HISTORICAL EXPERIMENT ON GROWTH RATE

13. 26
14. Darwin's Discussion of the Data 26
15. Galton's Method of Interpretation 28
16. Pairing and Grouping 31
17. " Student's " t Test 33
18. Fallacious Use of Statistics 37
19. Manipulation of the Data 39
20. Validity and Randomisation 40
21. Test of a Wider Hypothesis 43

IV. AN AGRICULTURAL EXPERIMENT IN RANDOMISED BLOCKS

PAGE

22. Description of the Experiment 48
23. Statistical Analysis of the Observations 50
24. Precision of the Comparisons 56
25. The Purposes of Replication 58
26. Validity of the Estimation of Error 60
27. Bias of Systematic Arrangements 62
28. Partial Elimination of Error 63
29. Shape of Blocks and Plots 64
30. Practical Example 65

V. THE LATIN SQUARE

31. Randomisation subject to Double Restriction 68
32. The Estimation of Error 71
33. Faulty Treatment of Square Designs 72
34. Systematic Squares 74
35. Græco-Latin and Higher Squares 78
35·01. Configurations in Three or more Dimensions . . . 83
35·1. An Exceptional Design 86
36. Practical Exercises 88

VI. THE FACTORIAL DESIGN IN EXPERIMENTATION

37. The Single Factor 91
38. A Simple Factorial Scheme 93
39. The Basis of Inductive Inference 99
40. Inclusion of Subsidiary Factors 100
41. Experiments without Replication 104

VII. CONFOUNDING

42. The Problem of Controlling Heterogeneity 107
43. Example with 8 Treatments, Notation 109
44. Design suited to Confounding the Triple Interaction . . 111
45. Effect on Analysis of Variance 112
45·1. General System of Confounding in Powers of 2 . . . 114
45·2. Double Confounding 119
46. Example with 27 Treatments 120
47. Partial Confounding 127
47·1. Practical Exercises 133

VIII. SPECIAL CASES OF PARTIAL CONFOUNDING

PAGE

48.   135
49. Dummy Comparisons   135
50. Interaction of Quantity and Quality   137
51. Resolution of Three Comparisons among Four Materials .   .   139
52. An Early Example   140
53. Interpretation of Results   150
54. An Experiment with 81 Plots   152

IX. THE INCREASE OF PRECISION BY CONCOMITANT MEASUREMENTS. STATISTICAL CONTROL

55. Occasions suitable for Concomitant Measurements .   .   .   161
56. Arbitrary Corrections   166
57. Calculation of the Adjustment   169
58. The Test of Significance   173
58·1. Missing Values   175
59. Practical Examples   178

X. THE GENERALISATION OF NULL HYPOTHESES. FIDUCIAL PROBABILITY

60. Precision regarded as Amount of Information   .   .   .   182
61. Multiplicity of Tests of the same Hypothesis   185
62. Extension of the t Test   189
62·1. Fiducial Limits of a Ratio   192
63. The χ^2 Test   193
64. Wider Tests based on the Analysis of Variance   .   .   .   196
65. Comparisons with Interactions   204

XI. THE MEASUREMENT OF AMOUNT OF INFORMATION IN GENERAL

66. Estimation in General   209
67. Frequencies of Two Alternatives   211
68. Functional Relationships among Parameters   213
69. The Frequency Ratio in Biological Assay   .   .   .   219
70. Linkage Values inferred from Frequency Ratios   .   .   .   221
71. Linkage Values inferred from the Progeny of Self-fertilised or Intercrossed Heterozygotes   226
72. Information as to Linkage derived from Human Families.   .   231
73. The Information elicited by Different Methods of Estimation   .   234
74. The Information lost in the Estimation of Error   .   .   .   237
INDEX   242

I AM very sorry, *Pyrophilus*, that to the many (elsewhere enumerated) difficulties which you may meet with, and must therefore surmount, in the serious and effectual prosecution of experimental philosophy I must add one discouragement more, which will perhaps as much surprise as dishearten you ; and it is, that besides that you will find (as we elsewhere mention) many of the experiments published by authors, or related to you by the persons you converse with, false and unsuccessful (besides this, I say), you will meet with several observations and experiments which, though communicated for true by candid authors or undistrusted eye-witnesses, or perhaps recommended by your own experience, may, upon further trial, disappoint your expectation, either not at all succeeding constantly, or at least varying much from what you expected.

ROBERT BOYLE, 1673, *Concerning the Unsuccessfulness of Experiments.*

LE seul moyen de prévenir ces écarts, consiste à supprimer, ou au moins à simplifier, autant qu'il est possible, le raisonnement qui est de nous, & qui peut seul nous égarer, à la mettre continuellement a l'épreuve de l'expérience ; à ne conserver que les faits qui sont des vérites données par la nature, & qui ne peuvent nous tromper ; à ne chercher la verité que dans l'enchaînement des expériences & des observations, sur-tout dans l'ordre dans lequel elles sont présentées, de la même manière que les mathématiciens parviennent à la solution d'un problème par le simple arrangement des données, & en réduisant le raisonnement à des opérations si simples, à des jugemens si courts, qu'ils ne perdent jamais de vue l'évidence qui leur sert de guide.

Methode de Nomenclature chimique,
A. L. LAVOISIER, 1787.

THE DESIGN OF EXPERIMENTS

I

INTRODUCTION

1. The Grounds on which Evidence is Disputed

WHEN any scientific conclusion is supposed to be proved on experimental evidence, critics who still refuse to accept the conclusion are accustomed to take one of two lines of attack. They may claim that the *interpretation* of the experiment is faulty, that the results reported are not in fact those which should have been expected had the conclusion drawn been justified, or that they might equally well have arisen had the conclusion drawn been false. Such criticisms of interpretation are usually treated as falling within the domain of *statistics*. They are often made by professed statisticians against the work of others whom they regard as ignorant of or incompetent in statistical technique ; and, since the interpretation of any considerable body of data is likely to involve computations, it is natural enough that questions involving the logical implications of the results of the arithmetical processes employed, should be relegated to the statistician. At least I make no complaint of this convention. The statistician cannot evade the responsibility for understanding the processes he applies or recommends. My immediate point is that the questions involved can be dissociated from all that is strictly technical in the statistician's craft, and, *when so detached*, are questions only of the right use of

A

human reasoning powers, with which all intelligent people, who hope to be intelligible, are equally concerned, and on which the statistician, as such, speaks with no special authority. The statistician cannot excuse himself from the duty of getting his head clear on the principles of scientific inference, but equally no other thinking man can avoid a like obligation.

The other type of criticism to which experimental results are exposed is that the experiment itself was ill designed, or, of course, badly executed. If we suppose that the experimenter did what he intended to do, both of these points come down to the question of the *design*, or the *logical structure* of the experiment. This type of criticism is usually made by what I might call a heavyweight *authority*. Prolonged experience, or at least the long possession of a scientific reputation, is almost a pre-requisite for developing successfully this line of attack. Technical details are seldom in evidence. The authoritative assertion " His *controls* are *totally* inadequate " must have temporarily discredited many a promising line of work ; and such an authoritarian method of judgment must surely continue, human nature being what it is, so long as theoretical notions of the principles of experimental design are lacking— notions just as clear and explicit as we are accustomed to apply to technical details.

Now the essential point is that the two sorts of criticism I have mentioned are aimed only at different aspects of the same whole, although they are usually delivered by different sorts of people and in very different language. If the design of an experiment is faulty, any method of interpretation which makes it out to be decisive must be faulty too. It is true that there are a great many experimental procedures which are well designed in that they *may* lead to decisive conclusions, but on other occasions may fail to do so ; in such cases, if decisive conclusions are in fact drawn when they are unjustified, we may say that the fault is wholly in the interpretation, not in the design. But the fault of interpretation, even in these cases, lies in overlooking the characteristic features of the design which lead to the result being sometimes inconclusive, or conclusive on some questions but not on all. To understand correctly the one aspect of the problem is to understand the other. Statistical procedure and experimental design are only two different aspects of the same whole, and that whole comprises all the logical requirements of the complete process of adding to natural knowledge by experimentation.

2. The Mathematical Attitude towards Induction

In the foregoing paragraphs the subject-matter of this book has been regarded from the point of view of an experimenter, who wishes to carry out his work competently, and having done so wishes to safeguard his results, so far as they are validly established, from ignorant criticism by different sorts of superior persons. I have assumed, as the experimenter always does assume, that it *is* possible to draw valid inferences from the results of experimentation ; that it is possible to argue from consequences to causes, from observations to hypotheses ; as a statistician would say, from a sample to the population from which the sample was drawn, or, as a logician might put it, from the particular to the general. It is, however, certain that many mathematicians, if pressed on the point, would say that it is not possible rigorously to argue from the particular to the general ; that all such arguments must involve some sort of guesswork, which they might admit to be plausible guesswork, but the rationale of which, they would be unwilling, as mathematicians, to discuss. We may at once admit that any inference from the particular to the general must be attended with some degree of uncertainty, but this is not the same as to admit that such inference cannot be absolutely rigorous, for the nature and degree of the uncertainty may itself be capable of rigorous expression. In the theory of probability, as developed in its application to games of chance, we have the classic example proving this possibility. If the gamblers' apparatus are really *true* or unbiased, the probabilities of the different possible events, or combinations of events, can be inferred by a rigorous deductive argument, although the outcome of any particular game is recognised to be uncertain. The mere fact that inductive inferences are uncertain cannot, therefore, be accepted as precluding perfectly rigorous and unequivocal inference.

Naturally, writers on probability have made determined efforts to include the problem of inductive inference within the ambit of the theory of mathematical probability, developed in discussing deductive problems arising in games of chance. To illustrate how much was at one time thought to have been achieved in this way, I may quote a very lucid statement by Augustus de Morgan, published in 1838, in the preface to his essay on probabilities in *The Cabinet Cyclopædia*. At this period confidence in the theory of inverse probability, as it was called, had reached, under the influence of Laplace, its highest point. Boole's criticisms had not yet been made, nor the more decided rejection of the theory by Venn, Chrystal, and later writers. De Morgan is speaking of the advances in the theory which were leading to its wider application to practical problems.

" There was also another circumstance which stood in the way of the first investigators, namely, the not having considered, or, at least, not having discovered the method of reasoning from the happening of an event to the probability of one or another cause. The questions treated in the third chapter of this work could not therefore be attempted by them. Given an hypothesis presenting the necessity of one or another out of a certain, and not very large, number of consequences, they could determine the chance that any given one or other of those consequences should arrive ; but given an event as having happened, and which might have been the consequence of either of several different causes, or explicable by either of several different hypotheses, they could not infer the probability with which the happening of the event should cause the different hypotheses to be viewed. But, just as in natural philosophy the selection of an hypothesis by means of observed facts is always preliminary to any attempt at deductive discovery ; so in the application of the notion of probability to the actual affairs of life, the process of reasoning from observed events to their most probable antecedents must go before the direct use of any such antecedent, cause, hypothesis, or whatever it may be correctly termed. These two obstacles, therefore, the mathematical difficulty, and the want of an inverse method, prevented the science from extending its views beyond problems of that simple nature which games of chance present."

Referring to the inverse method, he later adds: " This was first used by the Rev. T. Bayes, and the author, though now almost forgotten, deserves the most honourable remembrance from all who treat the history of this science."

3. The Rejection of Inverse Probability

Whatever may have been true in 1838, it is certainly not true to-day that Thomas Bayes is almost forgotten. That he seems to have been the first man in Europe to have seen the importance of developing an exact and quantitative theory of inductive reasoning, of arguing from observational facts to the theories which might explain them, is surely a sufficient claim to a place in the history of science. But he deserves honourable remembrance for one fact, also, in addition to those mentioned by de Morgan. Having perceived the problem and devised an axiom which, if its truth were granted, would bring inverse inferences within the scope of the theory of mathematical probability, he was sufficiently critical of its validity to withhold his entire treatise from publication until his doubts should have been satisfied. In the event, the work was published after his death by his friend, Price, and we cannot say what views he ultimately held on the subject.

The discrepancy of opinion among historical writers on probability is so great that to mention the subject is unavoidable. It would, however, be out of place here to argue the point in detail. I will only state three considerations which will explain why, in the practical applications of the subject, I shall not assume the truth of Bayes' axiom. Two of these reasons would, I think, be generally admitted, but the first, I can well imagine, might be indignantly repudiated in some quarters. The first is this : The axiom leads to apparent mathematical contradictions. In explaining these contradictions away, advocates of inverse probability seem forced to regard mathematical probability, not as an objective quantity measured by observed frequencies, but as measuring -merely psychological tendencies, theorems respecting which are useless for scientific purposes.

My second reason is that it is the nature of an axiom that its truth should be apparent to any rational mind which fully apprehends its meaning. The axiom of Bayes has certainly been fully apprehended by a good many rational minds, including that of its author, without carrying this conviction of necessary truth. This, alone, shows that it cannot be accepted as the axiomatic basis of a rigorous argument.

My third reason is that inverse probability has been only very rarely used in the justification of conclusions from experimental facts, although the theory has been widely taught, and is widespread in the literature of probability. Whatever the reasons are which give experimenters confidence that they can draw valid conclusions from their results, they seem to act just as powerfully whether the experimenter has heard of the theory of inverse probability or not.

4. The Logic of the Laboratory

In fact, in the course of this book, I propose to consider a number of different types of experimentation, with especial reference to their logical structure, and to show that when the appropriate precautions are taken to make this structure complete, entirely valid inferences may be drawn from them, without using the disputed axiom. *If* this can be done, we shall, in the course of studies having directly practical aims, have overcome the theoretical difficulty of inductive inferences.

Inductive inference is the only process known to us by which essentially new knowledge comes into the world. To make clear the authentic conditions of its validity is the kind of contribution to the intellectual development of mankind which we should expect

experimental science would ultimately supply. Men
have always been capable of some mental processes of
the kind we call " learning by experience." Doubtless
this experience was often a very imperfect basis, and
the reasoning processes used in interpreting it were very
insecure ; but there must have been in these processes
a sort of embryology of knowledge, by which new
knowledge was gradually produced. Experimental
observations are only experience carefully planned in
advance, and designed to form a secure basis of new
knowledge ; that is, they are systematically related to
the body of knowledge already acquired, and the results
are deliberately observed, and put on record accurately.
As the art of experimentation advances the principles
should become clear by virtue of which this planning
and designing achieve their purpose.

It is as well to remember in this connection that the
principles and method of even *deductive* reasoning were
probably unknown for several thousand years after the
establishment of prosperous and cultured civilisations.
We take a knowledge of these principles for granted,
only because geometry is universally taught in schools.
The method and material taught is essentially that of
Euclid's text-book of the third century B.C., and no
one can make any progress in that subject without
thoroughly familiarising his mind with the requirements
of a precise deductive argument. Assuming the axioms,
the body of their logical consequences is built up
systematically and without ambiguity. Yet it is certainly
something of an accident historically that this particular
discipline should have become fashionable in the Greek
Universities, and later embodied in the curricula of
secondary education. It would be difficult to overstate
how much the liberty of human thought has owed to
this fortunate circumstance. Since Euclid's time there

have been very long periods during which the right of unfettered individual judgment has been successfully denied in legal, moral, and historical questions, but in which it has, none the less, survived, so far as purely deductive reasoning is concerned, within the shelter of apparently harmless mathematical studies.

The liberation of the human intellect must, however, remain incomplete so long as it is free only to work out the consequences of a prescribed body of dogmatic data, and is denied the access to unsuspected truths, which only direct observation can give. The development of experimental science has therefore done much more than to multiply the technical competence of mankind ; and if, in these introductory lines, I have seemed to wander far from the immediate purpose of this book, it is only because the two topics with which we shall be concerned, the arts of experimental design and of the valid interpretation of experimental results, in so far as they can be technically perfected, must constitute the core of this claim to the exercise of full intellectual liberty.

The chapters which follow are designed to illustrate the principles which are common to all experimentation, by means of examples chosen for the simplicity with which these principles are brought out. Next, to exhibit the principal designs which have been found successful in that field of experimentation, namely agriculture, in which questions of design have been most thoroughly studied, and to illustrate their applicability to other fields of work. Many of the most useful designs are extremely simple, and these deserve the greatest attention, as showing in what ways, and on what occasions, greater elaboration may be advantageous. The careful reader should be able to satisfy himself not only, in detail, *why* some experiments have a complex structure, but also *how* a complex observational record may be handled with intelligibility and precision.

The subject is a new one, and in many ways the most that the author can hope is to suggest possible lines of attack on the problems with which others are confronted. Progress in recent years has been rapid, and the few sections devoted to the subject in the author's *Statistical Methods for Research Workers*, first published in 1925, have, with each succeeding edition, come to appear more and more inadequate. On purely statistical questions the reader must be referred to that book. The present volume is an attempt to do more thorough justice to the problems of planning and foresight with which the experimenter is confronted.

REFERENCES AND OTHER READING

T. BAYES (1763). An essay towards solving a problem in the doctrine of chances. Phil. Trans. Roy. Soc., liii. 370.

A. DE MORGAN (1838). An essay on probabilities and on their application to life contingencies and insurance offices. Preface, vi. Longman & Co.

R. A. FISHER (1930). Inverse probability. Proc. Cambridge Phil. Soc., xxvi. 528-535.

R. A. FISHER (1932). Inverse probability and the use of likelihood. Proc. Cambridge Phil. Soc., xxviii. 257-261.

R. A. FISHER (1935). The logic of inductive inference. Journal Royal Statistical Society, xcviii. 39-54.

R. A. FISHER (1936). Uncertain inference. Am. Acad. of Arts and Sciences.

II

THE PRINCIPLES OF EXPERIMENTATION, ILLUSTRATED BY A PSYCHO-PHYSICAL EXPERIMENT

5. Statement of Experiment

A LADY declares that by tasting a cup of tea made with milk she can discriminate whether the milk or the tea infusion was first added to the cup. We will consider the problem of designing an experiment by means of which this assertion can be tested. For this purpose let us first lay down a simple form of experiment with a view to studying its limitations and its characteristics, both those which appear to be essential to the experimental method, when well developed, and those which are not essential but auxiliary.

Our experiment consists in mixing eight cups of tea, four in one way and four in the other, and presenting them to the subject for judgment in a random order. The subject has been told in advance of what the test will consist, namely that she will be asked to taste eight cups, that these shall be four of each kind, and that they shall be presented to her in a random order, that is in an order not determined arbitrarily by human choice, but by the actual manipulation of the physical apparatus used in games of chance, cards, dice, roulettes, etc., or, more expeditiously, from a published collection of random sampling numbers purporting to give the actual results of such manipulation. Her task is to divide the 8 cups into two sets of 4, agreeing, if possible, with the treatments received.

6. Interpretation and its Reasoned Basis

In considering the appropriateness of any proposed experimental design, it is always needful to forecast all possible results of the experiment, and to have decided without ambiguity what interpretation shall be placed upon each one of them. Further, we must know by what argument this interpretation is to be sustained. In the present instance we may argue as follows. There are 70 ways of choosing a group of 4 objects out of 8. This may be demonstrated by an argument familiar to students of " permutations and combinations," namely, that if we were to choose the 4 objects in succession we should have successively 8, 7, 6, 5 objects to choose from, and could make our succession of choices in $8 \times 7 \times 6 \times 5$, or 1680 ways. But in doing this we have not only chosen every possible set of 4, but every possible set in every possible order ; and since 4 objects can be arranged in order in $4 \times 3 \times 2 \times 1$, or 24 ways, we may find the number of possible choices by dividing 1680 by 24. The result, 70, is essential to our interpretation of the experiment. At best the subject can judge rightly with every cup and, knowing that 4 are of each kind, this amounts to choosing, out of the 70 sets of 4 which might be chosen, that particular one which is correct. A subject without any faculty of discrimination would in fact divide the 8 cups correctly into two sets of 4 in one trial out of 70, or, more properly, with a frequency which would approach 1 in 70 more and more nearly the more often the test were repeated. Evidently this frequency, with which unfailing success would be achieved by a person lacking altogether the faculty under test, is calculable from the number of cups used. The odds could be made much higher by enlarging the experiment, while, if the experiment were much smaller even the greatest possible success would give odds so low that the result might, with considerable probability, be ascribed to chance.

7. The Test of Significance

It is open to the experimenter to be more or less exacting in respect of the smallness of the probability he would require before he would be willing to admit that his observations have demonstrated a positive result. It is obvious that an experiment would be useless of which no possible result would satisfy him. Thus, if he wishes to ignore results having probabilities as high as 1 in 20—the probabilities being of course reckoned from the hypothesis that the phenomenon to be demonstrated is in fact absent—then it would be useless for him to experiment with only 3 cups of tea of each kind. For 3 objects can be chosen out of 6 in only 20 ways, and therefore complete success in the test would be achieved without sensory discrimination, *i.e.* by " pure chance," in an average of 5 trials out of 100. It is usual and convenient for experimenters to take 5 per cent. as a standard level of significance, in the sense that they are prepared to ignore all results which fail to reach this standard, and, by this means, to eliminate from further discussion the greater part of the fluctuations which chance causes have introduced into their experimental results. No such selection can eliminate the whole of the possible effects of chance coincidence, and if we accept this convenient convention, and agree that an event which would occur by chance only once in 70 trials is decidedly " significant," in the statistical sense, we thereby admit that no isolated experiment, however significant in itself, can suffice for the experimental demonstration of any natural pheno-menon ; for the " one chance in a million " will undoubtedly occur, with no less and no more than its appropriate frequency, however surprised we may be that it should occur to *us*. In order to assert that a natural phenomenon is experimentally demonstrable we need, not an isolated record, but a reliable method of procedure. In relation to the test of significance, we may say that a phenomenon is experimentally demonstrable when we know how to conduct an experiment which will rarely fail to give us a statistically significant result.

Returning to the possible results of the psycho-physical experiment, having decided that if every cup were rightly classified a significant positive result would be recorded, or, in other words, that we should admit that the lady had made good her claim, what should be our conclusion if, for each kind of cup, her judgments are 3 right and 1 wrong? We may take it, in the present discussion, that any error in one set of judgments will be compensated by an error in the other, since it is known to the subject that there are 4 cups of each kind. In enumerating the number of ways of choosing 4 things out of 8, such that 3 are right and 1 wrong, we may note that the 3 right may be chosen, out of the 4 available, in 4 ways and, independently of this choice, that the 1 wrong may be chosen, out of the 4 available, also in 4 ways. So that in all we could make a selection of the kind supposed in 16 different ways. A similar argument shows that, in each kind of judgment, 2 may be right and 2 wrong in 36 ways, 1 right and 3 wrong in 16 ways and none right and 4 wrong in 1 way only. It should be noted that the frequencies of these five possible results of the experiment make up together, as it is obvious they should, the 70 cases out of 70.

It is obvious, too, that 3 successes to 1 failure, although showing a bias, or deviation, in the right direction, could not be judged as statistically significant evidence of a real sensory discrimination. For its frequency of chance occurrence is 16 in 70, or more than 20 per cent. Moreover, it is not the best possible result, and in judging of its significance we must take account not only of its own frequency, but also of the frequency of any better result. In the present instance " 3 right and 1 wrong " occurs 16 times, and " 4 right " occurs once in 70 trials, making 17 cases out of 70 as good as or better than that observed. The reason for including cases better than that observed becomes obvious on considering what our conclusions would have been had the case of 3 right and 1 wrong only 1 chance, and the case of 4 right 16 chances of occurrence out of 70. The rare case of 3 right and 1 wrong could not be judged significant merely because it was rare, seeing that a higher degree of success would frequently have been scored by mere chance.

8. The Null Hypothesis

Our examination of the possible results of the experiment has therefore led us to a statistical test of significance, by which these results are divided into two classes with opposed interpretations. Tests of significance are of many different kinds, which need not be considered here. Here we are only concerned with the fact that the easy calculation in permutations which we encountered, and which gave us our test of significance, stands for something present in every possible experimental arrangement ; or, at least, for something required in its interpretation. The two classes of results which are distinguished by our test of significance are, on the one hand, those which show a significant discrepancy from a certain hypothesis ; namely, in this case, the hypothesis that the judgments given are in no way influenced by the order in which the ingredients have been added ; and on the other hand, results which show no significant discrepancy from this hypothesis. This hypothesis, which may or may not be impugned by the result of an experiment, is again characteristic of all experimentation. Much confusion would often be avoided if it were explicitly formulated when the experiment is designed. In relation to any experiment we may speak of this hypothesis as the " null hypothesis," and it should be noted that the null hypothesis is never proved or established, but is possibly disproved, in the course of experimentation. Every experiment may be said to exist only in order to give the facts a chance of disproving the null hypothesis.

It might be argued that if an experiment can disprove the hypothesis that the subject possesses no sensory discrimination between two different sorts of object, it must therefore be able to prove the opposite hypothesis, that she can make some such discrimination. But this last hypothesis, however reasonable or true it may be, is ineligible as a null hypothesis to be tested by experiment, because it is inexact. If it were asserted that the subject would never be wrong in her judgments we should again have an exact hypothesis, and it is easy to see that this hypothesis could be disproved by a single failure, but could never be proved by any finite amount of experimentation. It is evident that the null hypothesis must be exact, that is free from vagueness and ambiguity, because it must supply the basis of the " problem of distribution," of which the test of significance is the solution. A null hypothesis may, indeed, contain arbitrary elements, and in more complicated cases often does so : as, for example, if it should assert that the death-rates of two groups of animals are equal, without specifying what these death-rates actually are. In such cases it is evidently the equality rather than any particular values of the death-rates that the experiment is designed to test, and possibly to disprove.

In cases involving statistical "estimation" these ideas may be extended to the simultaneous consideration of a series of hypothetical possibilities. The notion of an error of the so-called "second kind," due to accepting the null hypothesis "when it is false" may then be given a meaning in reference to the quantity to be estimated. It has no meaning with respect to simple tests of significance, in which the only available expectations are those which flow from the null hypothesis being true. Problems of the more elaborate type involving estimation are discussed in Chapter IX.

9. Randomisation ; the Physical Basis of the Validity of the Test

We have spoken of the experiment as testing a certain null hypothesis, namely, in this case, that the subject possesses no sensory discrimination whatever of the kind claimed ; we have, too, assigned as appropriate to this hypothesis a certain frequency distribution of occurrences, based on the equal frequency of the 70 possible ways of assigning 8 objects to two classes of 4 each ; in other words, the frequency distribution appropriate to a classification by pure chance. We have now to examine the physical conditions of the experimental technique needed to justify the assumption that, if discrimination of the kind under test is absent, the result of the experiment will be wholly governed by the laws of chance. It is easy to see that it might well be otherwise. If all those cups made with the milk first had sugar added, while those made with the tea first had none, a very obvious difference in flavour

B

would have been introduced which might well ensure that all those made with sugar should be classed alike. These groups might either be classified all right or all wrong, but in such a case the frequency of the critical event in which all cups are classified correctly would not be 1 in 70, but 35 in 70 trials, and the test of significance would be wholly vitiated.   Errors equivalent in principle to this are very frequently incorporated in otherwise well-designed experiments.

It is no sufficient remedy to insist that " all the cups must be exactly alike " in every respect except that to be tested.   For this is a totally impossible requirement in our example, and equally in all other forms of experimentation.   In practice it is probable that the cups will differ perceptibly in the thickness or smoothness of their material, that the quantities of milk added to the different cups will not be exactly equal, that the strength of the infusion of tea may change between pouring the first and the last cup, and that the temperature also at which the tea is tasted will change during the course of the experiment.   These are only examples of the differences probably present ; it would be impossible to present an exhaustive list of such possible differences appropriate to any one kind of experiment, because the uncontrolled causes which may influence the result are always strictly innumerable.   When any such cause is named, it is usually perceived that, by increased labour and expense, it could be largely eliminated.   Too frequently it is assumed that such refinements constitute improvements to the experiment.   Our view, which will be much more fully exemplified in later sections, is that it is an essential characteristic of experimentation that it is carried out with limited resources, and an essential part of the subject of experimental design to ascertain how these should be best applied ; or, in particular, to which causes of disturbance care should be given, and which *ought* to be deliberately ignored. To ascertain, too, for those which are not to be ignored, to what *extent* it is worth while to take the trouble to diminish their magnitude. For our present purpose, however, it is only necessary to recognise that, whatever degree of care and experimental skill is expended in equalising the conditions, other than the one under test, which are liable to affect the result, this equalisation must always be to a greater or less extent incomplete, and in many important practical cases will certainly be grossly defective. We are concerned, therefore, that this inequality, whether it be great or small, shall not impugn the exactitude of the frequency distribution, on the basis of which the result of the experiment is to be appraised.

10. The Effectiveness of Randomisation

The element in the experimental procedure which contains the essential safeguard is that the two modifications of the test beverage are to be prepared " in random order." This, in fact, is the only point in the experimental procedure in which the laws of chance, which are to be in exclusive control of our frequency distribution, have been explicitly introduced. The phrase " random order " itself, however, must be regarded as an incomplete instruction, standing as a kind of shorthand symbol for the full procedure of randomisation, by which the validity of the test of significance may be guaranteed against corruption by the causes of disturbance which have not been eliminated. To demonstrate that, with satisfactory randomisation, its validity is, indeed, wholly unimpaired, let us imagine all causes of disturbance—the strength of the infusion, the quantity of milk, the temperature at which it is tasted, etc.—to be predetermined for each cup ; then since these, on the null hypothesis, are the only causes influencing classification, we may say that the probabilities of each of the 70 possible choices or classifications which the subject can make are also predetermined. If, now, after the disturbing causes are fixed, we assign, strictly at random, 4 out of the 8 cups to each of our experimental treatments, then every set of 4, whatever its probability of being so classified, will certainly have a probability of exactly 1 in 70 of *being* the 4, for example, to which the milk is added first. However important the causes of disturbance may be, even if they were to make it certain that one particular set of 4 should receive this classification, the probability that the 4 so classified and the 4 which ought to have been so classified should be the same, must be rigorously in accordance with our test of significance.

It is apparent, therefore, that the random choice of the objects to be treated in different ways would be a complete guarantee of the validity of the test of significance, if these treatments were the last in time of the stages in the physical history of the objects which might affect their experimental reaction. The circumstance that the experimental treatments cannot always be applied last, and may come relatively early in their history, causes no practical inconvenience ; for subsequent causes of differentiation, if under the experimenter's control, as, for example, the choice of different pipettes to be used with different flasks, can either be predetermined before the treatments have been randomised, or, if this has not been done, can be randomised on their own account ; and other causes of differentiation will be either (*a*) consequences of differences already randomised, or (*b*) natural consequences of the difference in treatment to be tested, of which on the null hypothesis there will be none, by definition, or (c) effects supervening by chance independently from the treatments applied. Apart, therefore, from the avoidable error of the experimenter himself introducing with his test treatments, or subsequently, other differences in treatment, the effects of which the experiment is not intended to study, it may be said that the simple precaution of randomisation will suffice to guarantee the validity of the test of significance, by which the result of the experiment is to be judged.

11. The Sensitiveness of an Experiment. Effects of Enlargement and Repetition

A probable objection, which the subject might well make to the experiment so far described, is that only if every cup is classified correctly will she be judged successful. A single mistake will reduce her performance below the level of significance. Her claim, however, might be, not that she could draw the distinction with invariable certainty, but that, though sometimes mistaken, she would be right more often than not ; and that the experiment should be enlarged sufficiently, or repeated sufficiently often, for her to be able to demonstrate the predominance of correct classifications in spite of occasional errors.

An extension of the calculation upon which the test of significance was based shows that an experiment with 12 cups, six of each kind, gives, on the null hypothesis, 1 chance in 924 for complete success, and 36 chances for 5 of each kind classified right and 1 wrong. As 37 is less than a twentieth of 924, such a test could be counted as significant, although a pair of cups have been wrongly classified ; and it is easy to verify that, using larger numbers still, a significant result could be obtained with a still higher proportion of errors. By increasing the size of the experiment, we can render it more sensitive, meaning by this that it will allow of the detection of a lower degree of sensory discrimination, or, in other words, of a quantitatively smaller departure from the null hypothesis. Since in every case the experiment is capable of disproving, but never of proving this hypothesis, we may say that the value of the experiment is increased whenever it permits the null hypothesis to be more readily disproved.

The same result could be achieved by repeating the experiment, as originally designed, upon a number of different occasions, counting as a success all those occasions on which 8 cups are correctly classified. The chance of success on each occasion being 1 in 70, a simple application of the theory of probability shows that 2 or more successes in 10 trials would occur, by chance, with a frequency below the standard chosen for testing significance ; so that the sensory discrimination would be demonstrated, although, in 8 attempts out of 10, the subject made one or more mistakes. This procedure may be regarded as merely a second way of enlarging the experiment and, thereby, increasing its sensitiveness, since in our final calculation we take account of the aggregate of the entire series of results, whether successful or unsuccessful. It would clearly be illegitimate, and would rob our calculation of its basis, if the unsuccessful results were not all brought into the account.

12. Qualitative Methods of increasing Sensitiveness

Instead of enlarging the experiment we may attempt to increase its sensitiveness by qualitative improvements ; and these are, generally speaking, of two kinds : (a) the reorganisation of its structure, and (b) refinements of technique. To illustrate a change of structure we

might consider that, instead of fixing in advance that
4 cups should be of each kind, determining by a random
process how the subdivision should be effected, we
might have allowed the treatment of each cup to be
determined independently by chance, as by the toss of
a coin, so that each treatment has an equal chance of
being chosen. The chance of classifying correctly
8 cups randomised in this way, without the aid of sensory
discrimination, is 1 in 2^8, or 1 in 256 chances, and there
are only 8 chances of classifying 7 right and 1 wrong ;
consequently the sensitiveness of the experiment has
been increased, while still using only 8 cups, and it is
possible to score a significant success, even if one is
classified wrongly. In many types of experiment,
therefore, the suggested change in structure would be
evidently advantageous. For the special requirements
of a psycho-physical experiment, however, we should
probably prefer to forego this advantage, since it would
occasionally occur that all the cups would be treated
alike, and this, besides bewildering the subject by an
unexpected occurrence, would deny her the real advantage of judging by comparison.

Another possible alteration to the structure of the
experiment, which would, however, decrease its sensitiveness, would be to present determined, but unequal,
numbers of the two treatments. Thus we might arrange
that 5 cups should be of the one kind and 3 of the other,
choosing them properly by chance, and informing the
subject how many of each to expect. But since the
number of ways of choosing 3 things out of 8 is only
56, there is now, on the null hypothesis, a probability
of a completely correct classification of 1 in 56. It
appears in fact that we cannot by these means do better
than by presenting the two treatments in equal numbers,
and the choice of this equality is now seen to be

justified by its giving to the experiment its maximal sensitiveness.

With respect to the refinements of technique, we have seen above that these contribute nothing to the validity of the experiment, and of the test of significance by which we determine its result. They may, however, be important, and even essential, in permitting the phenomenon under test to manifest itself. Though the test of significance remains valid, it may be that without special precautions even a definite sensory discrimination would have little chance of scoring a significant success. If some cups were made with India and some with China tea, even though the treatments were properly randomised, the subject might not be able to discriminate the relatively small difference in flavour under investigation, when it was confused with the greater differences between leaves of different origin. Obviously, a similar difficulty could be introduced by using in some cups raw milk and in others boiled, or even condensed milk, or by adding sugar in unequal quantities. The subject has a right to claim, and it is in the interests of the sensitiveness of the experiment, that gross differences of these kinds should be excluded, and that the cups should, not as far as *possible*, but as far as is practically convenient, be made alike in all respects except that under test.

How far such experimental refinements should be carried is entirely a matter of judgment, based on experience. The validity of the experiment is not affected by them. Their sole purpose is to increase its sensitiveness, and this object can usually be achieved in many other ways, and particularly by increasing the size of the experiment. If, therefore, it is decided that the sensitiveness of the experiment should be increased, the experimenter has the choice between different methods of obtaining equivalent results ; and will be wise to choose whichever method is easiest to him, irrespective of the fact that previous experimenters may have tried, and recommended as very important, or even essential, various ingenious and troublesome precautions.

REFERENCES AND OTHER READING

R. A. FISHER (1925-1941). Statistical methods for research workers. Chap. III., §§ 15-19

R. A. FISHER (1926). The arrangement of field experiments. Journal of Ministry of Agriculture, xxxiii. 503-513.

III

A HISTORICAL EXPERIMENT ON GROWTH RATE

13. WE have illustrated a psycho-physical experiment, the result of which depends upon judgments, scored "right" or "wrong," and may be appropriately interpreted by the method of the classical theory of probability. This method rests on the enumeration of the frequencies with which different combinations of right or wrong judgments will occur, on the hypothesis to be tested. We may now illustrate an experiment in which the results are expressed in quantitative measures, and which is appropriately interpreted by means of the theory of errors.

In the introductory remarks to his book on "The effects of cross and self-fertilisation in the vegetable kingdom," Charles Darwin gives an account of the considerations which guided him in the design of his experiments and in the presentation of his data, which will serve well to illustrate the principles on which biological experiments may be made conclusive. The passage is of especial interest in illustrating the extremely crude and unsatisfactory statistical methods available at the time, and the manner in which careful attention to commonsense considerations led to the adoption of an experimental design, in itself greatly superior to these methods of interpretation.

14. Darwin's Discussion of the Data

"I long doubted whether it was worth while to give the measurements of each separate plant, but have decided to do so, in order that it may be seen that the superiority of the crossed plants over the self-fertilised does not commonly depend on the presence of two or three extra fine plants on the one side, or of a few very poor plants on the other side. Although several observers have insisted in general terms on the offspring from intercrossed varieties being superior to either parent-form, no precise measurements have been given ; and I have met with no observations on the effects of crossing and self-fertilising the individuals of the same variety. Moreover, experiments of this kind require so much time—mine having been continued during eleven years—that they are not likely soon to be repeated.

" As only a moderate number of crossed and self-fertilised plants were measured, it was of great importance to me to learn how far the averages were trustworthy. I therefore asked Mr Galton, who has had much experience in statistical researches, to examine some of my tables of measurements, seven in number, namely those of *Ipomœa*, *Digitalis*, *Reseda lutea*, *Viola*, *Limnanthes*, *Petunia*, and *Zea*. I may premise that if we took by chance a dozen or score of men belonging to two nations and measured them, it would I presume be very rash to form any judgment from such small numbers on their average heights. But the case is somewhat different with my crossed and self-fertilised plants, as they were of exactly the same age, were subjected from first to last to the same conditions, and were descended from the same parents. When only from two to six pairs of plants were measured, the results are manifestly of little or no value, except in so far as they confirm and are confirmed by experiments made on a larger scale with other species. I will now give the report on the seven tables of measurements which Mr Galton has had the great kindness to draw up for me."

15. Galton's Method of Interpretation

" I have examined the measurements of the plants with care, and by many statistical methods, to find out how far the means of the several sets represent constant realities, such as would come out the same so long as the general conditions of growth remained unaltered. The principal methods that were adopted are easily explained by selecting one of the shorter series of plants, say of *Zea mays*, for an example.

" The observations as I received them are shown in columns II. and III., where they certainly have no *primâ facie* appearance of regularity. But as soon as we arrange them in the order of their magnitudes, as in columns IV. and V., the case is materially altered. We now see, with few exceptions, that the largest plant on the crossed side in each pot exceeds the largest plant on the self-fertilised side, that the second exceeds the second, the third the third, and so on. Out of the fifteen cases in the table, there are only two exceptions to this rule.* We may therefore confidently affirm that a crossed series will always be found to exceed a self-fertilised series, within the range of the conditions under which the present experiment has been made.

" Next as regards the numerical estimate of this excess. The mean values of the several groups are so discordant, as is shown in the table just given, that a fairly precise numerical estimate seems impossible. But the consideration arises, whether the difference between pot and pot may not be of much the same order of importance as that of the other conditions upon which the growth of the plants has been modified. If so, and only on that condition, it would follow that when all the measurements, either of the crossed or the self-fertilised plants, were combined into a single series, that series would be statistically regular. The experiment is tried in columns VII. and VIII., where the regularity is abundantly clear, and justifies us in considering its mean as perfectly reliable.

* Galton evidently did not notice that this is true also before rearrangement.

TABLE I

Zea mays (young plants)

| | As recorded by Mr Darwin | | Arranged in Order of Magnitude | | | | |
| | | | In Separate Pots. | | In a Single Series. | | |
Column I.	II. Crossed.	III. Self-fert.	IV. Crossed.	V. Self-fert.	VI. Crossed.	VII. Self-fert.	VIII. Difference.
	Inches.	Inches.	Inches.	Inches.	Inches.	Inches.	Inches.
Pot I.	$23\frac{4}{8}$	$17\frac{3}{8}$	$23\frac{4}{8}$	$20\frac{3}{8}$	$23\frac{4}{8}$	$20\frac{3}{8}$	$-3\frac{1}{8}$
	12	$20\frac{3}{8}$	21	20	$23\frac{2}{8}$	20	-3
	21	20	12	$17\frac{8}{8}$	23	20	-3
Pot II.	22	20	22	20	$22\frac{1}{8}$	$18\frac{5}{8}$	$-3\frac{4}{8}$
	$19\frac{1}{8}$	$18\frac{3}{8}$	$21\frac{4}{8}$	$18\frac{5}{8}$	22	$18\frac{5}{8}$	-3
	$21\frac{4}{8}$	$18\frac{5}{8}$	$19\frac{8}{8}$	$18\frac{3}{8}$	22	$18\frac{3}{8}$	$-3\frac{4}{8}$
Pot III.	$22\frac{1}{8}$	$18\frac{5}{8}$	$23\frac{2}{8}$	$18\frac{5}{8}$	$21\frac{5}{8}$	18	$-3\frac{4}{8}$
	$20\frac{3}{8}$	$15\frac{2}{8}$	$22\frac{1}{8}$	18	21	18	-3
	$18\frac{2}{8}$	$16\frac{4}{8}$	$21\frac{5}{8}$	$16\frac{4}{8}$	21	$17\frac{3}{8}$	$-3\frac{5}{8}$
	$21\frac{5}{8}$	18	$20\frac{3}{8}$	$16\frac{2}{8}$	$20\frac{7}{8}$	$16\frac{4}{8}$	$-3\frac{7}{8}$
	$23\frac{2}{8}$	$15\frac{2}{8}$	18	$15\frac{8}{8}$	$19\frac{4}{8}$	$16\frac{2}{8}$	$-2\frac{6}{8}$
Pot IV.	21	18	23	18	$18\frac{4}{8}$	$15\frac{4}{8}$	$-2\frac{2}{8}$
	$22\frac{1}{8}$	$12\frac{6}{8}$	$22\frac{1}{8}$	18	12	$15\frac{2}{8}$	$+3$
	23	$15\frac{4}{8}$	21	$15\frac{4}{8}$	12	$12\frac{6}{8}$	$+0\frac{6}{8}$
	12	18	12	$12\frac{6}{8}$	…	…	…

I have protracted these measurements, and revised them in the usual way, by drawing a curve through them with a free hand, but the revision barely modifies the means derived from the original observations. In the present, and in nearly all the other cases, the difference between the original and revised means is under 2 per cent. of their value. It is a very remarkable coincidence that in the seven kinds of plants, whose measurements I have examined, the ratio between the heights of the crossed and of the self-fertilised ranges in five cases within very narrow limits. In *Zea mays* it is as 100 to 84, and in the others it ranges between 100 to 76 and 100 to 86.

TABLE 2

Pot.	Crossed.	Self-fert.	Difference.
I. . . .	18$\frac{7}{8}$	19$\frac{2}{8}$	+0$\frac{3}{8}$
II. . . .	20$\frac{7}{8}$	19	−1$\frac{7}{8}$
III. . .	21$\frac{1}{8}$	16$\frac{7}{8}$	−4$\frac{2}{8}$
IV. . .	19$\frac{6}{8}$	16	−3$\frac{6}{8}$

" The determination of the variability (measured by what is technically called the ' probable error ') is a problem of more delicacy than that of determining the means, and I doubt, after making many trials, whether it is possible to derive useful conclusions from these few observations. We ought to have measurements of at least fifty plants in each case, in order to be in a position to deduce fair results. . . ."

" Mr Galton sent me at the same time graphical representations which he had made of the measurements, and they evidently form fairly regular curves. He appends the words ' very good ' to those of *Zea* and *Limnanthes*. He also calculated the average height of the crossed and self-fertilised plants in the seven tables by a more correct method than that followed by me, namely, by including the heights, as estimated in accordance with statistical rules, of a few plants which died before they were measured ; whereas I merely added up the heights of the survivors, and divided the sum by their number. The difference in our results is in one way highly satisfactory, for the average heights of the self-fertilised plants, as deduced by Mr Galton, is less than mine in all the cases excepting one, in which our averages are the same ; and this shows that I have by no means exaggerated the superiority of the crossed over the self-fertilised plants."

16. Pairing and Grouping

It is seen that the method of comparison adopted by Darwin is that of pitting each self-fertilised plant against a cross-fertilised one, in conditions made as equal as possible. The pairs so chosen for comparison had germinated at the same time, and the soil conditions in which they grew were largely equalised by planting in the same pot. Necessarily they were not of the same parentage, as it would be difficult in maize to self-fertilise two plants at the same time as raising a cross-fertilised progeny from the pair. However, the parents were presumably grown from the same batch of seed. The evident object of these precautions is to increase the sensitiveness of the experiment, by making such differences in growth rate as were to be observed as little as possible dependent from environmental circumstances, and as much as possible, therefore, from intrinsic differences due to their mode of origin.

The method of pairing, which is much used in modern biological work, illustrates well the way in which an appropriate experimental design is able to reconcile two desiderata, which sometimes appear to be in conflict. On the one hand we require the utmost uniformity in the biological material, which is the subject of experiment, in order to increase the sensitiveness of each individual observation; and, on the other, we require to multiply the observations so as to demonstrate as far as possible the reliability and consistency of the results. Thus an experimenter with field crops may desire to replicate his experiments upon a large number of plots, but be deterred by the consideration that his facilities allow him to sow only a limited area on the same day. An experimenter with small mammals may have only a limited supply of an inbred and highly uniform stock, which he believes to be particularly desirable for experimental purposes. Or, he may desire to carry out his experiments on members of the same litter, and feel that his experiment is limited by the size of the largest litter he can obtain. It has indeed frequently been argued that, beyond a certain moderate degree, further replication can give no further increase in precision, owing to the increasing heterogeneity with which, it is thought, it must be accompanied. In all these cases, however, and in the many analogous cases which constantly arise, there is no real dilemma. Uniformity is only requisite between the objects whose response is to be contrasted (that is, objects treated differently). It is not requisite that all the parallel plots under the same treatment shall be sown on the same day, but only that each such plot shall be sown as far as possible simultaneously with the differently treated plot or plots with which it is to be compared. If, therefore, only two kinds of treatments are under examination, pairs of plots may be chosen, one plot for each treatment; and the precision of the experiment will be given its highest value if the members of each pair are treated closely alike, but will gain nothing from similarity of treatment applied to different pairs, nor lose anything if the conditions in these are somewhat varied. In the same way, if the numbers of animals available from any inbred line are too few for adequate replication, the experimental contrasts in treatments may be applied to pairs of animals from different inbred lines, so long as each pair belongs to the same line. In these two cases it is evident that the principle of combining similarity between controls to be compared, with diversity between parallels, may be extended to cases where three or more treatments are under investigation. The requirement that animals to be contrasted must come from the same litter limits, not the amount of replication, but the number of different treatments that can be so tested. Thus we might test three, but not so easily four or five treatments, if it were necessary that each set of animals must be of the same sex and litter. Paucity of homogeneous material limits the number of different treatments in an experiment, not the number of replications. It may cramp the scope and comprehensiveness of an experimental enquiry, but sets no limit to its possible precision.

17. "Student's" *t* Test *

Owing to the historical accident that the theory of errors, by which quantitative data are to be interpreted, was developed without reference to experimental methods, the vital principle has often been overlooked that the actual and physical conduct of an experiment must govern the statistical procedure of its interpretation. In using the theory of errors we rely for our conclusion upon one or more estimates of error, derived from the data, and appropriate to the one or more sets

* A full account of this test in more varied applications, and the tables for its use, will be found in *Statistical Methods for Research Workers*. Its originator, who published anonymously under the pseudonym " Student," possesses the remarkable distinction that, without being a professed mathematician, he made early in life this revolutionary refinement of the classical theory of errors.

C

of comparisons which we wish to make. Whether these estimates are valid, for the purpose for which we intend them, depends on what has been actually done. It is possible, and indeed it is all too frequent, for an experiment to be so conducted that no valid estimate of error is available. In such a case the experiment cannot be said, strictly, to be capable of proving anything. Perhaps it should not, in this case, be called an *experiment* at all, but be added merely to the body of *experience* on which, for lack of anything better, we may have to base our opinions. All that we need to emphasise immediately is that, if an experiment does allow us to calculate a valid estimate of error, its structure must completely determine the statistical procedure by which this estimate is to be calculated. If this were not so, no interpretation of the data could ever be unambiguous ; for we could never be sure that some other equally valid method of interpretation would not lead to a different result.

The object of the experiment is to determine whether the difference in origin between inbred and cross-bred plants influences their growth rate, as measured by height at a given date ; in other words, if the numbers of the two sorts of plants were to be increased indefinitely, our object is to determine whether the average heights, to which these two aggregates of plants will tend, are equal or unequal. The most general statement of our null hypothesis is, therefore, that the limits to which these two averages tend are equal. The theory of errors enables us to test a somewhat more limited hypothesis, which, by wide experience, has been found to be appropriate to the metrical characters of experimental material in biology. The disturbing causes which introduce discrepancies in the means of measurements of similar material are found to produce quantitative effects which conform satisfactorily to a theoretical distribution known as the normal law of frequency of error. It is this circumstance that makes it appropriate to choose, as the null hypothesis to be tested, one for which an exact statistical criterion is available, namely that the two groups of measurements are samples drawn from the same normal population. On the basis of this hypothesis we may proceed to compare the average difference in height, between the cross-fertilised and the self-fertilised plants, with such differences as might be expected between these averages, in view of the observed discrepancies between the heights of plants of like origin.

We must now see how the adoption of the method of pairing determines the details of the arithmetical procedure, so as to lead to an unequivocal interpretation. The pairing procedure, as indeed was its purpose, has equalised any differences in soil conditions, illumination, air-currents, etc., in which the several pairs of individuals may differ. Such differences having been eliminated from the experimental comparisons, and contributing nothing to the real errors of our experiment, must, for this reason, be eliminated likewise from our estimate of error, upon which we are to judge what differences between the means are compatible with the null hypothesis, and what differences are so great as to be incompatible with it. We are therefore not concerned with the differences in height among plants of like origin, but only with differences in height between members of the same pair, and with the discrepancies among these differences observed in different pairs. Our first step, therefore, will be to subtract from the height of each cross-fertilised plant the height of the self-fertilised plant belonging to the same pair. The differences are shown below in eighths of an inch.

With respect to these differences our null hypothesis asserts that they are normally distributed about a mean value at zero, and we have to test whether our 15 observed differences are compatible with the supposition that they are a sample from such a population.

TABLE 3

Differences in eighths of an inch between cross- and self-fertilised plants of the same pair

49	23	56
−67	28	24
8	41	75
16	14	60
6	29	−48

The calculations needed to make a rigorous test of the null hypothesis stated above involve no more than the sum, and the sum of the squares, of these numbers. The sum is 314, and, since there are 15 plants, the mean difference is $20\frac{14}{15}$ in favour of the cross-fertilised plants. The sum of the squares is 26,518, and from this is deducted the product of the total and the mean, or 6573, leaving 19,945 for the sum of squares of deviations from the mean, representing discrepancies among the differences observed in the 15 pairs. The algebraic fact here used is that

$$S(x-\bar{x})^2 = S(x^2) - \bar{x}S(x)$$

where S stands for summation over the sample, and $\bar{x}$ for the mean value of the observed differences, x.

We may make from this measure of the discrepancies an estimate of a quantity known as the *variance* of an individual difference, by dividing by 14, one less than the number of pairs observed. Equally, and what is more immediately required, we may make an estimate of the variance of the mean of 15 such pairs, by dividing again by 15, a process which yields 94·976 as the estimate.

The square root of the variance is known as the standard error, and it is by the ratio which our observed mean difference bears to its standard error that we shall judge of its significance. Dividing our difference, 20·933, by *its* standard error 9·746, we find this ratio (which is usually denoted by *t*) to be 2·148.

The object of these calculations has been to obtain from the data a quantity measuring the average difference in height between the cross-fertilised and the self-fertilised plants, in terms of the observed discrepancies among these differences ; and which, moreover, shall be distributed in a known manner when the null hypothesis is true. The mathematical distribution for our present problem was discovered by " Student " in 1908, and depends only upon the number of independent comparisons (or the number of degrees of freedom) available for calculating the estimate of error. With 15 observed differences we have among them 14 independent discrepancies, and our degrees of freedom are 14. The available tables of the distribution of *t* show that for 14 degrees of freedom the value 2·145 is exceeded by chance, either in the positive or negative direction, in exactly 5 per cent. of random trials. The observed value of *t*, 2·148, thus just exceeds the 5 per cent. point, and the experimental result may be judged significant, though barely so.

18. Fallacious Use of Statistics

We may now see that Darwin's judgment was perfectly sound, in judging that it was of importance to learn how far the averages were trustworthy, and that this could be done by a statistical examination of the tables of measurements of individual plants, though not of their averages. The example chosen, in fact, falls just on the border-line between those results which can suffice by themselves to establish the point at issue, and those which are of little value except in so far as they confirm or are confirmed by other experiments of a like nature. In particular, it is to be noted that Darwin recognised that the reliability of the result must be judged by the consistency of the superiority of the crossed plants over the self-fertilised, and not only on the difference of the averages, which might depend, as he says, on the presence of two or three extra-fine plants on the one side, or of a few very poor plants on the other side; and that therefore the presentation of the experimental evidence depended essentially on giving the measurements of each independent plant, and could not be assessed from the mere averages.

It may be noted also that Galton's scepticism of the value of the probable error, deduced from only 15 pairs of observations, though, as it turned out, somewhat excessive, was undoubtedly right in principle. The standard error (of which the probable error is only a conventional fraction) can only be estimated with considerable uncertainty from so small a sample, and, prior to " Student's " solution of the problem, it was by no means clear to what extent this uncertainty would invalidate the test of significance. From " Student's " work it is now known that the cause for anxiety was not so great as it might have seemed. Had the standard error been known with certainty, or derived from an effectively infinite number of observations, the 5 per cent. value of t would have been 1·960. When our estimate is based upon only 15 differences, the 5 per cent. value, as we have seen, is 2·145, or less than 10 per cent. greater. Even using the inexact theory available at the time, a calculation of the probable error would have provided a valuable guide to the interpretation of the results.

19. Manipulation of the Data

A much more serious fallacy appears to be involved in Galton's assumption that the value of the data, for the purpose for which they were intended, could be increased by rearranging the comparisons. Modern statisticians are familiar with the notions that any finite body of data contains only a limited amount of information, on any point under examination ; that this limit is set by the nature of the data themselves, and cannot be increased by any amount of ingenuity expended in their statistical examination : that the statistician's task, in fact, is limited to the extraction of the whole of the available information on any particular issue. If the results of an experiment, as obtained, are in fact irregular, this evidently detracts from their value ; and the statistician is not elucidating but falsifying the facts, who rearranges them so as to give an artificial appearance of regularity.

In rearranging the results of Darwin's experiment it appears that Galton thought that Darwin's experiment would be equivalent to one in which the heights of pairs of contrasted plants had been those given in his columns headed VI. and VII., and that the reliability of Darwin's average difference of about $2\frac{5}{8}$ inches could be fairly judged from the constancy of the 15 differences shown in column VIII.

How great an effect this procedure, if legitimate, would have had on the significance of the result, may be seen by treating these artificial differences as we have treated the actual differences given by Darwin. Applying the same arithmetical procedure as before, we now find t equals 5·171, a value which would be exceeded by chance only about once or twice in 10,000 trials, and is far beyond the level of significance ordinarily required. The falsification, inherent in this mode of procedure, will be appreciated if we consider that the tallest plant, of either the crossed or the self-fertilised series, will have become the tallest by reason of a number of favourable circumstances, including among them those which produce the discrepancies between those pairs of plants, which were actually grown together. By taking the difference between these two favoured plants we have largely eliminated real causes of error which have affected the value of our observed mean. We have, in doing this, grossly violated the principle that the estimate of error must be based on the effects of the very same causes of variation as have produced the real errors in our experiment. Through this fallacy Galton is led to speak of the mean as perfectly reliable, when, from its standard error, it appears that a repetition of the experiment would often give a mean quite 50 per cent. greater or less than that observed in this case.

20. Validity and Randomisation

Having decided that, when the structure of the experiment consists in a number of independent comparisons between pairs, our estimate of the error of the average difference must be based upon the discrepancies between the differences actually observed, we must next enquire what precautions are needed in the practical conduct of the experiment to guarantee that such an estimate shall be a valid one ; that is to say that the very same causes that produce our real error shall also contribute the materials for computing an estimate of it. The logical necessity of this requirement is readily apparent, for, if causes of variation which do not influence our real error are allowed to affect our estimate of it, or equally, if causes of variation affect the real error in such a way as to make no contribution to our

estimate, this estimate will be vitiated, and will be
incapable of providing a correct statement as to the
frequency with which our real error will exceed any
assigned quantity ; and such a statement of frequency
is the sole purpose for which the estimate is of any use.
Nevertheless, though its logical necessity is easily
apprehended, the question of the validity of the estimates
of error used in tests of significance was for long ignored,
and is still often overlooked in practice. One reason
for this is that standardised methods of statistical analysis
have been taken over ready-made from a mathematical
theory, into which questions of experimental detail do
not explicitly enter. In consequence the assumptions
which enter implicitly into the bases of the theory have
not been brought prominently under the notice of
practical experimenters. A second reason is that it has
not until recently been recognised that any simple
precaution would supply an absolute guarantee of the
validity of the calculations.

In the experiment under consideration, apart from
chance differences in the selection of seeds, the sole
source of the experimental error in the average of our
fifteen differences lies in the differences in soil fertility,
illumination, evaporation, etc., which make the site of
each crossed plant more or less favourable to growth
than the site assigned to the corresponding self-fertilised
plant. It is for this reason that every precaution, such
as mixing the soil, equalising the watering and orienting
the pot so as to give equal illumination, may be expected
to increase the precision of the experiment. If, now,
when the fifteen pairs of sites have been chosen, and in
so doing all the differences in environmental circumstances, to which the members of the different pairs
will be exposed during the course of the experiment,
have been predetermined, we then assign at random,

as by tossing a coin, which site shall be occupied by the
crossed and which by the self-fertilised plant, we shall
be assigning by the same act whether this particular
ingredient of error shall appear in our average with a
positive or a negative sign. Since each particular
error has thus an equal and independent chance of
being positive or negative, the error of our average
will necessarily be distributed in a sampling distribution,
centred at zero, which will be symmetrical in the sense
that to each possible positive error there corresponds
an equal negative error, which, as our procedure guaran-
tees, will in fact occur with equal probability.

Our estimate of error is easily seen to depend only
on the same fifteen ingredients, and the arithmetical
processes of summation, subtraction and division may
be designed, and have in fact been designed, so as to
provide the estimate appropriate to the system of
chances which our method of choosing sites had imposed
on the data. This is to say much more than merely
that the experiment is unbiased, for we might still call
the experiment unbiased if the whole of the cross-
fertilised plants had been assigned to the west side of
the pots, and the self-fertilised plants to the east side,
by a single toss of the coin. That this would be in-
sufficient to ensure the validity of our estimate may
be easily seen ; for it might well be that some unknown
circumstance, such as the incidence of different illumination at different times of the day, or the desiccating
action of the air-currents prevalent in the greenhouse,
might systematically favour all the plants on one side
over those on the other. The effect of any such pre-
vailing cause would then be confounded with the
advantage, real or apparent, of cross-breeding over
inbreeding, and would be eliminated from our estimate
of error, which is based solely on the discrepancies

between the differences shown by different pairs of plants. Randomisation properly carried out, in which each pair of plants are assigned their positions independently at random, ensures that the estimates of error will take proper care of all such causes of different growth rates, and relieves the experimenter from the anxiety of considering and estimating the magnitude of the innumerable causes by which his data may be disturbed. The one flaw in Darwin's procedure was the absence of randomisation.

Had the same measurements been obtained from pairs of plants properly randomised the experiment would, as we have shown, have fallen on the verge of significance. Galton was led greatly to overestimate its conclusiveness through the major error of attempting to estimate the reliability of the comparisons by rearranging the two series in order of magnitude. His discussion shows, in other respects, an over-confidence in the power of statistical methods to remedy the irregularities of the actual data. In particular, the attempt mentioned by Darwin to improve on the simple averages of the two series " by a more correct method . . . by including the heights, as estimated in accordance with statistical rules, of a few plants which died before they were measured," seems to go far beyond the limits of justifiable inference, and is one of many indications that the logic of statistical induction was in its infancy, even at a time when the technique of accurate experimentation had already been notably advanced.

21. Test of a Wider Hypothesis

It has been mentioned that " Student's " t test, in conformity with the classical theory of errors, is appropriate to the null hypothesis that the two groups of measurements are samples drawn from the same normally

distributed population. This is the type of null hypothesis which experimenters, rightly in the author's
opinion, usually consider it appropriate to test, for
reasons not only of practical convenience, but because
the unique properties of the normal distribution make
it alone suitable for general application. There has,
however, in recent years, been a tendency for theoretical
statisticians, not closely in touch with the requirements
of experimental data, to stress the element of normality,
in the hypothesis tested, as though it were a serious
limitation to the test applied. It is, indeed, demonstrable
that, as a test of this hypothesis, the exactitude of
" Student's " t test is absolute. It may, nevertheless,
be legitimately asked whether we should obtain a
materially different result were it possible to test the
wider hypothesis which merely asserts that the two
series are drawn from the same population, without
specifying that this is normally distributed.

In these discussions it seems to have escaped recognition that the physical act of randomisation, which, as
has been shown, is necessary for the validity of any
test of significance, affords the means, in respect of any
particular body of data, of examining the wider hypothesis in which no normality of distribution is implied.
The arithmetical procedure of such an examination is
tedious, and we shall only give the results of its application in order to show the possibility of an independent
check on the more expeditious methods in common use.

On the hypothesis that the two series of seeds are
random samples from identical populations, and that
their sites have been assigned to members of each pair
independently at random, the 15 differences of Table 3
would each have occurred with equal frequency with a
positive or with a negative sign. Their sum, taking
account of the two negative signs which have actually

occurred, is 314, and we may ask how many of the 2^{15} numbers, which may be formed by giving each component alternatively a positive and a negative sign, exceed this value. Since *ex hypothesi* each of these 2^{15} combinations will occur by chance with equal frequency, a knowledge of how many of them are equal to or greater than the value actually observed affords a direct arithmetical test of the significance of this value.

It is easy to see that if there were no negative signs, or only one, every possible combination would exceed 314, while if the negative signs are 7 or more, every possible combination will fall short of this value. The distribution of the cases, when there are from 2 to 6 negative values, is shown in the following table :—

TABLE 4

Number of combinations of differences, positive or negative, which exceed or fall short of the total observed

Number of negative values.	>314	= 314	<314	Total.
0 . . .	1	...	...	1
1 . . .	15	...	...	15
2 . . .	94	1	10	105
3 . . .	263	3	189	455
4 . . .	302	11	1,052	1,365
5 . . .	138	12	2,853	3,003
6 . . .	22	1	4,982	5,005
7 or more . .	...	...	22,819	22,819
Total . . .	835	28	31,905	32,768

In just 863 cases out of 32,768 the total deviation will have a positive value as great as or greater than that observed. In an equal number of cases it will have as great a negative value. The two groups together constitute 5·267 per cent. of the possibilities available, a result very nearly equivalent to that obtained using the t test with the hypothesis of a normally distributed population. Slight as it is, indeed, the difference between the tests of these two hypotheses is partly due to the continuity of the t distribution, which effectively counts only half of the 28 cases which give a total of exactly 314, as being as great as or greater than the observed value.

Both tests prove that, in about 5 per cent. of trials, samples from the same batch of seed would show differences just as great, and as regular, as those observed ; so that the experimental evidence is scarcely sufficient to stand alone. In conjunction with other experiments, however, showing a consistent advantage of cross-fertilised seed, the experiment has considerable weight ; since only once in 40 trials would a chance deviation have been observed both so large, and in the right direction.

How entirely appropriate to the present problem is the use of the distribution of t, based on the theory of errors, when accurately carried out, may be seen by inserting an adjustment, which effectively allows for the discontinuity of the measurements. This adjustment is not usually of practical importance, with the t test, and is only given here to show the close similarity of the results of testing the two hypotheses, in one of which the errors are distributed according to the normal law, whereas in the other they may be distributed in any conceivable manner. The adjustment * consists in calculating the value of t as though the total difference between the two sets of measurements were less than that actually observed by half a unit of grouping ;

---

* This adjustment is an extension to the distribution of t of Yates' adjustment for continuity, which is of greater importance in the distribution of χ^2, for which it was developed.

i.e. as if it were 313 instead of 314, since the possible values advance by steps of 2. The value of t is then found to be 2·139 instead of 2·148. The following table shows the effect of the adjustment on the test of significance, and its relation to the test of the more general hypothesis.

TABLE 5

		t.	Probability of a Positive Difference exceeding that observed.
Normal hypothesis { unadjusted	.	2·148	2·485 per cent.
adjusted	.	2·139	2·529 ,,
General hypothesis	. . . .	.	2·634 ,,

The difference between the two hypotheses is thus equivalent to little more than a probability of one in a thousand.

REFERENCES AND OTHER READING

C. DARWIN (1876). The effects of cross- and self-fertilisation in the vegetable kingdom. John Murray, London.

" STUDENT " (1908). The probable error of a mean. Biometrika, vi. 1-25.

R. A. FISHER (1925). Applications of " Student's " distribution. Metron, v. 90-104.

R. A. FISHER (1925-1941). Statistical methods for research workers. Chap. V., §§ 23-24.

IV

AN AGRICULTURAL EXPERIMENT IN
RANDOMISED BLOCKS

22. Description of the Experiment

IN pursuance of the principles indicated by the discussions in the previous chapters we may now take an example from agricultural experimentation, the branch of the subject in which these principles have so far been most explicitly developed, and in which the advantages and disadvantages of the different methods open to the experimenter may be most clearly discussed.

We will suppose that our experiment is designed to test the relative productivity, or yield, of five different varieties of a farm crop ; and that a decision has already been arrived at as to what produce shall be regarded as yield. In the case of cereal crops, for example, we may decide to measure the yield as total grain, or as grain sufficiently large not to pass a specified sieve, or as grain and straw valued together at predetermined prices, or in whatever method may be deemed appropriate for the purposes of the experiment. Our object is to determine whether, on the soil or in the climatic conditions experienced by the test, any of the varieties tested yield more than others, and, if so, to evaluate the differences with a determinate degree of precision.

We shall suppose that the experimental area is divided into eight compact, or approximately square, blocks, and that each of these is divided into five plots running from end to end of the block, and lying side by side, making forty plots in all. Apart from the differences in variety to be used, the whole area is to have uniform agricultural treatment. At harvest, narrow edges about a foot in width for cereal crops, or the width of a single row for larger plants, such as roots and potatoes, are to be discarded from experimental yields ; the central portions, cut to be of equal area, are to be harvested, and the produce weighed, or, if preferred, measured in some other manner.

In each block the five plots are assigned one to each of the five varieties under test, and this assignment is made at random. This does not mean that the experimenter writes down the names of the varieties, or letters standing for them, in any order that may occur to him, but that he carries out a physical experimental process of randomisation, using means which shall ensure that each variety has an equal chance of being tested on any particular plot of ground. A satisfactory method is to use a pack of cards numbered from 1 to 100, and to arrange them in random order by repeated shuffling. The varieties are then numbered from 1 to 5, and any card such as number 33, for example, is deemed to correspond to variety number 3, because on dividing by 5 this number is found as the remainder. Numbers divisible by 5 will correspond to variety number 5. The order of varieties in each block may then be quickly determined from the order of the cards in the pack, after thoroughly shuffling. The remainder corresponding to any variety is disregarded after its first occurrence in the block.

Since 5 is a divisor of a hundred, each variety will be represented by 20 cards, and the probabilities of each appearing in any particular place will be equal. If we had been randomising six varieties we should have used a number of cards divisible by 6, for example

D

96, and could, for this purpose, use the same pack as before, discarding the 4 cards numbers 97 to 100, or indeed, any other four cards the numbers of which leave the remainders 1, 2, 3 and 4 on dividing by 6.

To save the labour of card shuffling use is often made of printed tables of random sampling numbers, in which, for example, all numbers of 4 figures are arranged in random order. The first such table was published by Tippett; another is available in *Statistical Tables*. Starting at any point in such a table and proceeding in any direction, such as up or down the columns, or along the rows, we may take each pair of digits to represent the number of a card in the pack of 100, disregarding any which may be superfluous for our purpose. Using such means the process of randomisation is extremely rapid, and a chart showing the arrangement of the experiment may be prepared as quickly as if the varieties had been set out in a systematic order.

23. Statistical Analysis of the Observations

The arithmetical discussion by which the experiment is to be interpreted is known as the analysis of variance. This is a simple arithmetical procedure, by means of which the results may be arranged and presented in a single compact table, which shows both the structure of the experiment and the relevant results, in such a way as to facilitate the necessary tests of their significance. The structure of the experiment is determined when it is planned, and before the content of its results, consisting of the actual yields from the different plots, is known. It depends on the number of varieties to be compared, on the number of replications of each obtainable, and on the system by which these are arranged; in our present example in randomised blocks. In its arithmetical aspect this structure is specified by the numbers of degrees of freedom, or of independent comparisons, which can be made between the plots, or relevant groups of plots. Between 40 plots 39 independent comparisons can be made, and so the total number of degrees of freedom will be 39. This number will be divided into 3 parts representing the numbers of independent comparisons (*a*) between varieties, (*b*) between blocks, and (*c*) representing the discrepancies between the relative performances of different varieties in different blocks, which discrepancies provide a basis for the estimation of error. We may specify the structure of our typical experiment by a partition of the total of 39 degrees of freedom into these three parts as under.

TABLE 6

Structure of an Experiment in Randomised Blocks

Varieties	4
Blocks	7
Error	28
Total . . .	39

It is easy to see that the number of degrees of freedom for any group of simple comparisons, such as those between varieties or between blocks, must be 1 less than the number of items to be compared. In the present instance, in which the plots are assigned within the blocks wholly at random, the whole of the remaining 28 degrees of freedom are due simply to differences in fertility between different plots within the same block, and are therefore available for providing the estimate of error. As will be explained more fully later, many more complicated modes of subdivision of the total number of degrees of freedom may be employed, and will be appropriate to more complicated forms of experimental enquiry. The form we have set out is appropriate to the question whether the yields given by the different varieties show, as a whole, greater differences than would ordinarily be found, had only a single variety been sown on the same land. It is appropriate to test the null hypothesis that our 5 varieties give in fact equal yields.

The completion of the analysis of variance, when the yields are known, must be strictly in accordance with the structure imposed by the design of the experiment, and consists in the partition of a quantity known as the *sum of squares* (*i.e.* of deviations from the mean) into the same three parts as those into which we have already divided the degrees of freedom. Our data consists of 40 yields (y), 5 from each block and 8 from each variety which, for further calculation, can be conveniently arranged in a table of 5 columns and 8 lines.

TABLE 7

Scheme for calculation of totals and means

					Total	Mean
—	—	—	—	—	A	a
—	—	—	—	—	B	b
—	—	—	—	—	C	c
—	—	—	—	—	D	d
—	—	—	—	—	E	e
—	—	—	—	—	F	f
—	—	—	—	—	G	g
—	—	—	—	—	H	h
Total P	Q	R	S	T	M	
Mean p	q	r	s	t		m

The totals of the five columns will then represent the totals of the yields obtained from the 5 varieties, and may be designated by the capital letters P, Q, R, S and T. The mean yields from the five varieties, found by dividing these by 8, will be designated by small letters p, q, r, s and t. In like manner the totals of the rows will represent the total yields harvested from each of the blocks of land used ; we shall denote these by A, B, C, D, E, F, G, H, and the corresponding means by a, b, c, d, e, f, g, h. Evidently, the totals of the rows and the totals of the columns are sub-totals of the same grand total, denoted by M, from which the general mean m is derived by dividing by 40. The arrangement is illustrated in Table 7 ; also Table 7A, p. 66, gives some numerical observations in this form.

The sum of squares of deviations from the mean, which, in the analysis of variance, is to be divided into portions corresponding to varieties, blocks and error, is found by adding together the squares of the 40 recorded yields, and deducting the product Mm. The difference, which corresponds to the total 39 degrees of freedom, is actually the sum of the squares of the 40 differences or deviations between the actual yields, y, and their general mean, m ; it therefore measures the total amount of variation due to all causes, observed between our different plots. The method we have given, however, for obtaining this quantity is convenient for our purpose, for the product Mm is used also in our calculation of the other entries of the table, which are indeed rapidly obtainable once the total sum of squares is known. The portion, for example, corresponding to the 4 degrees of freedom between varieties is found simply by summing the products Pp+ Qq+ . . ., and deducting Mm. Similarly, the portion ascribable to the 7 degrees of freedom between blocks is obtained by summing the products Aa+Bb+Cc . . ., and deducting Mm. Knowing the contributions to the sum of

squares of these 11 degrees of freedom, the amount
corresponding to the remaining 28 degrees of freedom,
due to error, may be found by subtraction from the
total.   In this way the total sum of squares, representing
the total amount of variation due to all causes between
the 40 yields of the experiment, is divided into the 3
portions relevant to its interpretation, measuring respectively the amount of variation between varieties, the
amount of variation between blocks, and the amount of
discrepancy between the performances of the different
varieties in the different blocks.   The greater part of
the arithmetical labour is accomplished with the calculation of the total sum of squares.

Corresponding to the three sums of squares into
which the total has been partitioned, we may now
calculate the mean squares, by dividing each by the
corresponding number of degrees of freedom.   On the
null hypothesis the mean squares for variety and error
have the particularly simple interpretation that each
may be regarded as an independent estimate of the
same single quantity, the variance due to error of a single
plot.   If the varieties had in fact the same yield the
mean square derived from the 4 degrees of freedom of
varieties would have, on the average, the same value
as that derived from the 28 degrees of freedom for error.
In any one trial these values would indeed differ, but
only by errors of random sampling.   The relative
precision of our estimates is determined solely by the
number of degrees of freedom upon which each is based,
so that, knowing these numbers, the ratio of any two
estimates affords a test of significance.   In other words,
on the null hypothesis the random sampling distribution
of this ratio is precisely known.   Thus, in our example,
it would happen just once in 20 trials that the estimate
based on 4 degrees of freedom exceeded that based on

28 degrees of freedom in a ratio greater than 2·714. If, therefore, the observed ratio exceeds this level, we have a measurable basis for confidence that the differences observed between the yields of the different varieties are not due wholly to the differences in fertility of the plots on which they were grown. Again, in only 1 per cent. of trials will the ratio exceed 4·074, a value which thus marks the level of a more severe test of significance. Since tests of the same kind will be required for all possible pairs of numbers of degrees of freedom, it is convenient for purposes of tabulation to use a criterion which varies more regularly than the arithmetical ratio employed in the illustrations above. It is usual, therefore, to carry out the calculation by using the natural logarithms of the mean squares, and since the difference of the two logarithms specifies the ratios of the corresponding numbers, the tables used in this test of significance give the values of a quantity, z, defined as half the difference between the natural logarithms obtained.

The z test may be regarded as an extension of the t test, appropriate to cases where more than two variants are to be compared. Like it, it is derived from the theory of errors, and is exact when the normal law of errors is realised. It is even less affected than the t test by such deviations from normality as are met with in practice. As with the t test, its appropriateness to any particular body of data may be verified arithmetically. Such verification is not ordinarily necessary and is always laborious. Often the number of random arrangements available is far too great for them to be examined exhaustively, as was done with Darwin's experiment in Chapter III. Eden and Yates have, however, published a method of obtaining rapidly the results of a large random selection of these arrangements, and have demonstrated how closely the theoretical distribution was verified in material that was far from normal.

24. Precision of the Comparisons

If the yields of the different varieties in the experiment fail to satisfy the test of significance they will not often need to be considered further, for the results, as so far tested, are compatible with the view that all differences observed in the experiment are due to variations in the fertility of the experimental area, and this is the simplest interpretation to put upon them. If, however, a significant value of z has been obtained the null hypothesis has been falsified, and may therefore be set aside. We shall thereafter proceed to interpret the differences between the varietal yields as due, at least in part, to the inherent qualities of the varieties, as manifested on the conditions of the test, and shall be concerned to know with what precision these different yields have been evaluated. For this purpose the mean square, corresponding to the 28 degrees of freedom assigned to error, is available as an estimate of the variance of a single plot due to the uncontrolled causes which constitute the errors of our determinations. From this fundamental estimate we may derive a corresponding estimate of the variance of the sum of the yields from 8 plots by multiplying by 8, or, if we prefer, we may derive the variance of the mean yield of 8 plots by dividing by 8. In either case the square root of the variance gives the standard deviation, and provides therefore a means of judging which of the differences among our varietal yield values are sufficiently great to be regarded as well established, and which are to be regarded as probably fortuitous. If the experiment leaves any grounds for practical doubt, values may be compared by the t test mentioned in Chapter II., remembering that our estimate of error is based on 28 degrees of freedom.

It is an advantage of arrangements in randomised blocks that, corresponding to any particular comparison contrast, the components of error appertaining to this comparison may be isolated. This is done simply by finding the difference in yield, or performance, between the treatments, or groups of treatments, to be compared, in each replication of the experiment. The discrepancies between these differences obtained from different replications, taking account of their signs, constitute the components of error appropriate to this comparison, which may now be tested by a t test, independently of the other comparisons which the experiment affords. Although fewer degrees of freedom are available for the estimation of error from these components only, their isolation affords an additional safeguard when, as may sometimes occur, some comparisons are, in reality, less accurately evaluated than others.

When the z test does not demonstrate significant differentiation, much caution should be used before claiming significance for special comparisons. Comparisons, which the experiment was designed to make, may, of course, be made without hesitation. It is comparisons suggested subsequently, by a scrutiny of the results themselves, that are open to suspicion ; for if the variants are numerous, a comparison of the highest with the lowest observed value, picked out from the results, will often appear to be significant, even from undifferentiated material. Properly, such unforeseen effects should be regarded only as suggestions for future experimentation, in which they can be deliberately tested. To form a preliminary opinion as to the strength of the evidence, it is sometimes useful to consider how many similar comparisons would have been from the start equally plausible. Thus, in comparing the best with the worst of ten tested varieties, we have chosen the pair with the largest apparent difference out of 45 pairs, which might equally have been chosen. We might, therefore, require the probability of the observed difference to be as small as 1 in 900, instead of 1 in 20, before attaching statistical significance to the contrast.

25. The Purposes of Replication

An examination of the structure of the standard type of agricultural experiment described above, and of the use made of its structure in the statistical process of interpretation, shows that the replication or repetition of the varieties tested on different plots of land serves two distinct purposes. It serves first to diminish the error, a purpose which has been widely recognised, though the manner in which it does so has not always been well understood. In our experiment the sampling variance of a mean yield was found by dividing the estimate of variance for a single plot by 8. Since the variance of a single plot would not be necessarily or systematically increased by increasing the number of blocks, the variance of our mean yields will generally fall off inversely to the number of replications included. In increasing the number of blocks, however, we should have increased the area of the experiment, and it is probable that this increase in area, even if we had used the same number of larger plots, would itself have served to diminish the experimental error. If the area of the experiment were kept constant and the replication increased by using smaller plots we should only gain in precision if, as abundant agricultural experiment shows to be generally the case, the greater proximity of the smaller areas led to a greater similarity in the fertility of the soil. The practical limit to plot subdivision is set, in agricultural experiments, by the necessity of discarding a strip at the edge of each plot. The width of the strip depends on the competition of neighbouring plants for moisture, soil nutrients and light, and is independent of the size of the plots. Consequently, as smaller plots are used, a larger proportion of the experimental area has to be discarded. The soil heterogeneity of most experimental land is, however, so pronounced that it is profitable to discard a considerable proportion of the area, in order to bring the experimental treatments or varieties to be contrasted more closely together than would otherwise be possible. With plants, such as potatoes and sugar-beets, where it is sufficient to discard a single row, one on each side of the plot, it has been repeatedly found that strips of 4 rows wide, of which only the central two are included in the yield, make a more economical use of a given experimental area than either wider or narrower plots would do.

Replication, therefore, in the sense of the comminution of the experimental area, down to plots of the most efficient size, has an important but limited part to play in increasing the precision of an experiment. It should not, in this connection, be overlooked that many other factors contribute to the same result, such as accuracy in harvesting and weighing the produce ; in measuring the areas of land harvested ; care in the choice of the experimental area ; in insuring the similarity of the treatment of its different parts ; in safeguarding the crop against damage, and its produce against loss. All these factors contribute to the precision of the experiment, and though, when the conditions are otherwise favourable, there can be no doubt that attention is rightly concentrated on diminishing the important causes of error due to variations in soil fertility, it is evident that, even in experiments in which these causes were almost wholly eliminated, neglect of common-sense precautions, which, none the less, require care and supervision, may lead to entirely unreliable results.

26. Validity of the Estimation of Error

Whereas replication of the experimental varieties or treatments on different plots, formed by the subdivision of the experimental area, is of value as one of the means of increasing the accuracy of the experimental comparisons, its main purpose, which there is no alternative method of achieving, is to supply an estimate of error by which the significance of these comparisons is to be judged. The need of such an estimate may be perceived by considering the doubts with which the interpretation of an experiment would be involved if it consisted only of a single plot for each treatment. The treatment giving the highest yield would of course appear to be the best, but no one could say whether the plot would not in fact have yielded as well under some or all of the other treatments. If, indeed, the difference in yield appeared large to the experimenters they might argue that so large a difference could not reasonably be ascribed to a difference in soil fertility, since it was contrary to their experience that neighbouring plots treated alike should differ so greatly. To enforce this argument they would in fact have to claim that their past experience had already furnished a basis for the estimation of error, which could be applied with confidence to the circumstances of the experiment under discussion. Even if this claim could be granted the experiment would carry with it the serious disadvantage that it would no longer be self-contained, but would depend for its interpretation from experience previously gathered. It could no longer be expected to carry conviction to others lacking this supplementary experience. How weak the evidence of such previous experience must always be will be seen by considering that, even if the identical area of the experiment, divided into the same plots, had been harvested under uniform treatment in previous years, it would need twenty years' experience to form even the roughest judgment as to how great a difference between the yields of any two plots would occur by chance as often as once in 20 trials. It is on the exactitude of our estimate of the magnitude of this difference that the precision of our test of significance must depend. Even such a tedious series of preliminary trials, moreover, could only supply a direct basis for the test of significance, if we could assume the absence of progressive changes, both in the weather and in the condition of the soil. This consideration effectively demonstrates that the accumulation of past experience, as a basis for testing significance, is as insecure in theory as it would be inconvenient in practice.

The impossibility of testing two or more treatments, in the same year, and on identically the same land, is not, however, an insuperable obstacle to exact experimentation. It is surmounted by testing the treatments not on identical land, but on random samples of the same experimental areas. From this aspect the appropriateness of a *random* assignment of the treatments to the different plots appears most inevitably. We shall need to judge of the magnitude of the differences introduced by testing our treatments upon different plots by the discrepancies between the performances of the same treatment in different blocks. Our estimate of error must be obtained by a comparison of plots treated alike, but it is to be applied to interpret the differences observed between sets of plots treated differently. The validity of our estimate of error for this purpose is guaranteed by the provision that any two plots, not in the same block, shall have the same probability of being treated alike, and the same probability of being treated differently in each of the ways in which this is possible. The purpose of randomisation in this, as in the previous experiments exemplified, is to guarantee the validity of the test of significance, this test being based on an estimate of error made possible by replication.

27. Bias of Systematic Arrangements

In any particular case it will probably be possible to assign sets of plots within an area to the several treatments so as to equalise their fertility more completely than is done by a random arrangement, and many systematic arrangements for doing this have from time to time been proposed. The effect of such a procedure on the test of significance may be seen by imagining it carried out on an area under uniform treatment, so that the actual yields are not at all affected by the reallocation of the plots. In the analysis of variance, therefore, the total sum of squares is unchanged, as is also the portion ascribable to blocks. If, therefore, the agronomist's ingenuity has been successful in diminishing the differences in fertility between treatments, the diminution of the sum of squares in that line of the table will have been exactly counterbalanced by an increase in the sum of squares upon which the estimate of error is based. The effect of the rearrangement will have been to diminish the real errors of the experiment, but at the expense of increasing the estimate of error ; so that, although the comparisons have really been improved in precision they will appear to have been less accurate than before, and less reliance will be placed on the result. In the opposite case, likewise, if by bad luck or bad judgment the systematic arrangement adopted has increased rather than lessened the real errors of the experiment, then the estimate of error will be even diminished, and will be, for both reasons, an under-estimate of the errors actually incurred. The results of using arrangements which differ from the random arrangement in either direction are thus in one way or the other undesirable. This is to be expected, since in both cases the estimate of error is vitiated, or rendered unreliable for the purpose for which it was made.

28. Partial Elimination of Error

It is to be noted that the restriction upon a purely random arrangement which has been imposed, by applying each treatment once only on each block of land, introduces no such disturbance of the validity of the estimate of error. For the differences in average fertility between the different blocks of land used, which have been, by this restriction, eliminated from our experimental comparisons, have been equally eliminated from our estimate of error in the analysis of variance. Prior to the introduction of this method it was, indeed, common for elements of error which had been carefully and thoroughly eliminated in the field to be reintroduced in the process of statistical estimation ; so that successful experimental arrangements were made to appear to be unsuccessful and *vice versâ*. The essential fact govern-ing our analysis is that the errors due to soil heterogeneity will be divided, by a good experiment, into two portions. The first, which is to be made as large as possible, will be completely eliminated, by the arrangement of the experiment, from the experimental comparisons, and will be as carefully eliminated in the statistical laboratory from the estimate of error. As to the remainder, which cannot be treated in this way, no attempt will be made to eliminate it in the field, but, on the contrary, it will be carefully randomised so as to provide a valid estimate of the errors to which the experiment is in fact liable.

29. Shape of Blocks and Plots

Having satisfied ourselves that replication, supplemented by randomisation, will afford a valid test of the significance of our comparisons, we may consider what modifications of our practical procedure will serve to increase the precision of these comparisons. If several areas of land are available for experiment some care may usually be given to choose one that appears to be uniform, as judged by the surface and texture of the soil, or by the appearance of a previous crop, though the value of such judgments by inspection, with which alone we are here concerned, appears to be very easily overrated. After choosing the area we usually have no guidance beyond the widely verified fact that patches in close proximity are commonly more alike, as judged by the yield of crops, than those which are further apart. Consequently, the division of the land into compact or approximately square blocks will usually result in the blocks being as much unlike as possible, while different areas within the same block will be more closely similar than if the blocks had been long and narrow. The effect of this upon the analysis of variance is to place as large a fraction as possible of the variance due to soil heterogeneity in the portion ascribable to variation between blocks, this portion being eliminated from our experimental error ; and to leave as little as possible in the variation within blocks, which supplies both our experimental errors and our estimate of them. It is therefore a safe rule to make the blocks as compact as possible.

With respect to our subdivision of the blocks into plots our object is exactly the opposite. The experimental error arises solely from differences between the areas chosen as plots within the same block. These differences must be made as small as possible, or, in other words, each plot must, so far as may be, sample fairly the whole area of the block in which it is placed.

It is often desirable, therefore, when it does not conflict with agricultural convenience in other ways, to let the plots lie side by side as narrow strips, each running the whole length of its block. It is not, however, in every type of experiment an advantage to use such elongated plots. Some important causes of soil heterogeneity, dependent from agricultural operations, affect the land in stripes. Elongated plots will then only be advantageous if they can be laid transversely to these stripes. When this would entail inconvenience, or additional labour in cutting the correct area, as in the case of strip plots with cereals, running across the drill rows, the labour available for the experiment may often be better applied by using square plots, and improving the accuracy in other ways. Plots of compact shape are, indeed, commonly used in experiments in randomised blocks, not because the theoretical advantage of using elongated strips, in one direction or the other, is not appreciated, but for the purely practical reason that to realise it by laying strips in the required direction would be a more costly method of increasing precision than other methods at the experimenter's disposal.

30. Practical Example

The following data show a comparison of the yields of five varieties of barley in an experiment arranged in randomised blocks, carried out in the State of Minnesota in the years 1930 and 1931 and reported by F. R. Immer, H. K. Hayes and Le Roy Powers in the *Journal of the American Society of Agronomy*. The experiment really

E

TABLE 7A

Total Yields of Barley Varieties in Twelve Independent Trials

Place and Year		Manchuria.	Svansota.	Velvet.	Trebi.	Peatland.	Total.	Mean.
1	1931	81·0	105·4	119·7	109·7	98·3	514·1	102·82
	1932	80·7	82·3	80·4	87·2	84·2	414·8	82·96
2	1931	146·6	142·0	150·7	191·5	145·7	776·5	155·30
	1932	100·4	115·5	112·2	147·7	108·1	583·9	116·78
3	1931	82·3	77·3	78·4	131·3	89·6	458·9	91·78
	1932	103·1	105·1	116·5	139·9	129·6	594·2	118·84
4	1931	119·8	121·4	124·0	140·8	124·8	630·8	126·16
	1932	98·9	61·9	96·2	125·5	75·7	458·2	91·64
5	1931	98·9	89·0	69·1	89·3	104·1	450·4	90·08
	1932	66·4	49·9	96·7	61·9	80·3	355·2	71·04
6	1931	86·9	77·1	78·9	101·8	96·0	440·7	88·14
	1932	67·7	66·7	67·4	91·8	94·1	387·7	77·54
Total .		1132·7	1093·6	1190·2	1418·4	1230·5	6065·4	
Mean .		94·3916	91·13	99·183	118·2	102·5416		101·09

dealt with ten varieties, of which five have been selected for this example. The blocks in the example are twelve separate experiments carried out at six locations in the State in the two years.

REFERENCES AND OTHER READING

T. EDEN and F. YATES (1933). On the validity of Fisher's *z* test when applied to an actual example of non-normal data. Journal of Agricultural Science, xxiii. 6-17.

R. A. FISHER (1924). On a distribution yielding the error functions of several well-known statistics. Proceedings of the International Mathematical Congress, Toronto, pp. 805-813.

R. A. FISHER (1925-41). Statistical methods for research workers. Chap. VIII. and the Table of *z*, Table VI.

F. R. IMMER, H. K. HAYES and LE ROY POWERS (1934). Statistical determination of barley varietal adaptation. Journal of the American Society of Agronomy, May, xxvi. 403-419.

L. H. C. TIPPETT (1927). Random sampling numbers. Tracts for computers, xv. Cambridge University Press.

R. A. FISHER and F. YATES (1938-48). Statistical Tables for biological, agricultural and medical research. Oliver and Boyd Ltd., Edinburgh.

V

THE LATIN SQUARE

31. Randomisation subject to Double Restriction

The subdivision of the area of an agricultural experiment into compact blocks, in each of which all the experimental treatments to be compared are equally represented, has been found to add greatly to the precision of the experimental comparisons obtainable by the expenditure of a fixed amount of labour, and supervisory care, to a limited area of land. An equally great advantage is obtained, in other fields of research, by a similar subdivision of the material into relatively homogeneous series, to each of which the different experimental treatments are applied in equal proportion. The extent of this gain is limited only by the degree of homogeneity which can be obtained within each series. It is an essential condition of experimentation that the experimental material is known to be variable, but it is not known, in respect of any individual, in what direction his response to a given treatment will vary from the average. No direct allowance for this variability can, therefore, be made. The knowledge which guides us in increasing the precision of an experiment is not a knowledge of the individual peculiarities of particular experimental units, such as plots of land, experimental animals, coco-nut palms, or hospital patients, but a knowledge that there is less variation within certain aggregates of these than there is among different individuals belonging to different aggregates. The recognition of criteria by which the experimental material may be fruitfully subdivided thus plays an important part in all types of quantitative experimentation.

It was first shown in experimental agriculture, though the principle has since been applied in other fields, that the process of subdivision might profitably be duplicated. This experimental principle is best illustrated by the arrangement known as the Latin square, a method which is singularly reliable in giving precise comparisons when the number of treatments (or varieties, etc.) to be compared is from 4 to 8. Suppose we wish to compare 6 treatments. The experimental area (which need not be an exact square in form, but should be a relatively compact rectangle) is divided into 36 equal plots lying in 6 rows and 6 columns. It is then a combinatorial fact that we can assign plots to the 6 treatments such that for each treatment one plot lies in each row and one in each column of the square. It is possible generally to do this in a large number of ways, for if we start with one solution of the problem, and rearrange the rows in it as wholes, in any of the ways in which these may be arranged, a large number of new solutions will be found. With a 6×6 square the rows may be rearranged in 720 ways, including that from which we start, so we have at once a set of 720 solutions. Equally, or consecutively, we may arrange the columns in 720 ways ; and, finally, we may do the same with the treatments, while still conserving the property which the Latin square was designed to possess. The process of transformation will generate a number of different solutions which varies according to the particular square from which we happen to start. The smallest transformation set comprises 1,728,000 solutions, while the 5 largest each comprise 93,312,000. If a solution is chosen at random from such a set each plot has an equal probability of receiving any of the possible treatments, and each pair of plots, not in the same row or column, has the same probability, namely one-fifth, of being treated alike.   The process of randomisation, necessary to ensure the validity of the test of significance applied to the experiment, consists in choosing one at random out of the set of squares which can be generated from any chosen arrangement.

The object of arranging plots in a Latin square is to eliminate from the experimental comparisons possible differences in fertility which may exist between whole rows of plots, and between whole columns of plots, as they stand in the field.   The need for such a double elimination was particularly apparent to agricultural experimenters owing to the fact that in many fields there is found to occur either a gradient of fertility across the whole area, or parallel strips of land having a higher or lower fertility than the average.   But, for particular fields, it is not known whether such hetero- geneity will be more pronounced in the one or the other direction in which the field is ordinarily cultivated. Such soil variations may be due in part to the past history of the field, such as the lands in which it has been laid up for drainage producing variations in the depth and present condition of the soil, or to portions of it having been manured or cropped otherwise than the remainder ; but whatever the causes, the effects are sufficiently widespread to make apparent the importance of eliminating the major effects of soil heterogeneity, not only in one direction across the field, but at the same time in the direction at right angles to it.   This double elimination is effected by the Latin square arrangement, which combines the combinatorial fact stated above with the possibility of basing estimates of error upon an effective randomisation.

32. The Estimation of Error

As has been already illustrated in the experiment in randomised blocks, the error will be properly estimated only if the same components of heterogeneity which have been successfully eliminated by the arrangement in the field are also eliminated in the interpretation of the results in the laboratory. This elimination is carried out by an analysis of variance closely similar to that used in the last chapter. The 35 independent comparisons possible among 36 yields give 35 degrees of freedom. Of these, 5 are ascribable to differences between rows, and 5 to differences between columns. Thus 10 degrees of freedom serve to represent the components of heterogeneity, which have been eliminated in the field, and must be excluded from our estimate of error. Of the remaining 25 degrees of freedom, 5 represent differences between the treatments tested, and 20 represent components of error which have not been eliminated, but which have been carefully randomised so as to ensure that they shall contribute no more and no less than their share to the errors of our experimental comparisons.

The table shows the subdivision of the degrees of freedom for a 6×6 square, and in general for an $s \times s$ square used to test s treatments.

TABLE 8

	6×6 square.	$s \times s$ square.
Rows . . .	5	$s-1$
Columns . .	5	$s-1$
Treatments . .	5	$s-1$
Error . .	20	$(s-1)(s-2)$
Total . .	35	s^2-1

Corresponding to each part of the degrees of freedom the yield data of the experiment will provide a like

portion of the total of what we have called sum of
squares.   The first 3 portions may be calculated in
exactly the same way as are those for blocks and treatments in the randomised block arrangement.   Thus, if
the total yields in the rows are A, B, C, D, E, F, with
a grand total M, while the corresponding mean yields
are a, b, c, d, e, f, and m, the portion of the sum of squares
ascribable to rows is

$$aA+bB+cC+dD+eE+Ff-Mm.$$

The portions ascribable to columns and to treatments
are calculated similarly, while that ascribable to error
is calculated by deducting the 3 other items from the
total.   This total sum of squares, as in other cases, is
merely the sum of the squares of the deviations of the
yields of all individual plots from their general mean,
and may be calculated by subtracting mM from the
sum of the squares of these yields.

33. Faulty Treatment of Square Designs

When the possibility of effecting a double elimination
of errors due to soil heterogeneity was first realised, the
mistake was sometimes made of judging the precision
of the results merely from the observed discrepancies
between plots treated alike.   This would be correct
only if the whole 36 plots had been assigned at random,
and without restriction, to the 6 treatments.   Its effect
is that the 10 degrees of freedom corresponding to
rows and columns are included in the estimate of
error.   Thus what experimental design had gained in
the field arrangement was lost or thrown away in the
statistical analysis.   Indeed, by this method the apparent
precision of the experiment, and the consequent reliance
placed on its results, is less than if the treatments had

been assigned wholly at random, disregarding rows and columns, for the large components due to these have been excluded from the 5 degrees of freedom ascribed to treatments, and therefore contribute more than proportionately to the 30 remaining degrees of freedom, which on this system is regarded as error.

A fault of purely statistical origin also appears in some of the earlier work, namely, the use of the total number of plots, in place of the number of degrees of freedom, as a divisor in obtaining the estimated variance of the mean square. This may lead to the error being seriously underestimated. Apart from its arithmetical simplicity, the great advantage of arranging the statistical work in an analysis of variance lies in the safeguard it affords against errors of these two kinds. Once the degrees of freedom are subdivided it is apparent that the residue after allowing for rows, columns, and treatments has only 20 degrees of freedom, and once the contributions to the sum of squares due to rows and columns are identified and set aside, no one would think of introducing these in attempting to arrive at an estimate of error. The mean square, obtained by dividing the residual sum of squares by the degrees of freedom available for the estimation of error, is a valid estimate of the variance of the yield of a single plot, due to the components of error which have been randomised. The sampling variance of the total of six plots having the same treatment is found by multiplying the mean square by 6, and that of the mean of such plots, by dividing it by 6. The variance so obtained is itself liable to sampling errors, dependent on the number of degrees of freedom on which it is based. Since this number is often small, we should use the exact z test for testing the significance of the group of treatments as a whole. If it is desired to compare any two particular treatments, or to make any other simple contrast among the treatments employed, whether based on the totals or on the means, we obtain the sampling variance appropriate to the expression, find the standard error by taking the square root, and the ratio of the differences to be tested to its appropriate standard error will be the value of t, appropriate to test its significance, with the same number of degrees of freedom as that on which the estimate of variance was originally based. Readers unfamiliar with the statistical procedure of these tests are referred to *Statistical Methods for Research Workers*.

In agricultural trials a single Latin square will frequently give precision high enough to reduce the standard error to less than 2 per cent. of the yield, and sometimes to less than 1 per cent. If experimentation were only concerned with the comparison of four to eight treatments or varieties, it would therefore be not merely the principal but almost the universal design employed. It is particularly fitted for the comparison at a number of different places of a small selected group of highly qualified varieties, the relation of which to varying conditions of soil and weather needs to be explored. Where it fails is to provide a means of testing simultaneously a large number of different treatments or varieties. The means used to obtain precision in such experiments will be developed in later chapters.

34. Systematic Squares

When the idea of effecting an elimination of errors due to soil heterogeneity in two directions at right angles was first appreciated, the necessity for randomisation in experimental trials was not realised. In consequence, certain systematic arrangements were adopted. One

of these, which may be called a diagonal square, is
shown below :—

A	B	C	D	E
E	A	B	C	D
D	E	A	B	C
C	D	E	A	B
B	C	D	E	A

It will be observed that the conditions that one plot of
each kind lies in each row and one in each column are
satisfied by this arrangement.   The plots receiving
treatment A are, however, all in a line along the diagonal
of the square, and other lines parallel to this diagonal
also receive the same treatment throughout their length.
Consequently, there is ground to fear that if ridges or
strips of fertility run obliquely across the rows and
columns they may give to some of the treatments a
systematic advantage compared with the others.   In
other words, the components of soil fertility in which
the areas assigned to different treatments may differ,
may, not improbably, be larger than the remaining
components, representing differences between plots
treated alike, on which the estimate of error is based.
Consequently, if a systematic arrangement of this kind
is treated as though it were a Latin square two distinct
effects may be anticipated.   First, that the actual errors
in the comparisons of the treatments will be greater
than if a properly randomised Latin square had been
used, and, second, that the estimate of error obtained
from the experiment will be less, by reason of the
exclusion of the more important components of soil
variability, which have been confounded with the
treatments.

The first of these dangers was readily recognised,
though the second was ignored.   Consequently, an
improved systematic arrangement has been widely used.

It has been known in Denmark since about 1872, but is usually ascribed to the Norwegian, Knut Vik. The method is to move each row forward two places instead of one, giving the following pattern :—

$$
\begin{array}{ccccc}
A & B & C & D & E \\
D & E & A & B & C \\
B & C & D & E & A \\
E & A & B & C & D \\
C & D & E & A & B
\end{array}
$$

In this arrangement the areas bearing each treatment are nicely distributed over the experimental area, so as to exclude all probability that the more important components of soil heterogeneity should influence the comparison between treatments. This was clearly the intention of the arrangement ; but its fulfilment carries with it an unforeseen and unfortunate consequence. If, by the skill of the experimenter, the components of error, by which the comparisons between the treatments are affected are, on the average, less than those given by a random arrangement, it follows that those available for the estimation of error must be greater. This, as with randomised blocks, is easily seen by considering the subdivision of the sum of squares in the analysis of variance. The null hypothesis is that the treatments are without effect, and therefore that all the differences observed among the experimental results are due to experimental error. They are therefore unaffected by the arrangement adopted. The components ascribable to rows and columns, and eliminated from the experiment, are also the same however the plots may be arranged. Consequently, the total of the two components ascribed to treatments and to error, that is to say the true errors of our comparisons, and the estimate of these errors supplied by the experiment, have a total independent of the experimental arrangement. The sole effect of adopting one system of arrangement rather than another is on the manner in which the fixed total is divided between these two parts. The purpose of randomisation is to ensure that each degree of freedom shall have, on the null hypothesis, the same average content. Any method of arrangement, therefore, which diminishes the real errors must increase the apparent magnitude of these errors, by which the validity of the comparison is to be judged. The consequence is that not more but less reliance is placed, and must be placed, on the results, as a consequence of the experimenter's success in excluding the larger components of error from his comparisons.

It should be noted that this unfortunate consequence only ensues when a method of diminishing the real errors is adopted, unaccompanied by their elimination in the statistical analysis. Thus, when the treatments are equally distributed among the rows of an experiment, the real error is usually diminished, and the estimate of error may be diminished in the same measure by eliminating the differences between the different rows. The failure of systematic arrangements came from not recognising that the function of the experiment was not only to make an unbiased comparison, but to supply at the same time a valid test of its significance. This is vitiated equally whether the components affecting the comparisons are larger or smaller than those on which the estimate of error is based. The consequences of accepting an insignificant effect as significant, or of rejecting as insignificant one which, with sounder methods of experimentation, would have shown itself to be significant, are equally unfortunate. In fact, the calculation of standard errors is idle and misleading, if the method of arrangement adopted fails to guarantee

their validity, and the same applies to all other means
of testing significance.

The consequences surmised as to the effects of using
the two systematic squares illustrated above have in
fact been verified in detail by O. Tedin, by super-
imposing these arrangements, each 184 times, on the
yields obtained in uniformity trials, in which the null
hypothesis is known to be true ; and by comparing the
results with those obtained using random arrangements.
The discrepancies found are just what might have been
anticipated on theoretical grounds. The diagonal
square gives larger real errors accompanied by greater
apparent precision. The Knut Vik square gives lower
real errors accompanied by less apparent precision. It
is a curious fact that the bias of the Knut Vik square,
which was unsuspected, appears to be actually larger
than that of the diagonal square, which all experienced
experimenters would confidently recognise.

35. Græco-Latin and Higher Squares

The number of arrangements in a Latin square
is known for squares up to 7×7. Since the combinatorial properties which these illustrate are useful
in experimental design apart from their application
to the double elimination of error, it is well to know
something of them. The 2×2 square

A B
B A

illustrates the fact that the three independent contrasts
among 4 objects may be resolved into contrasts between
pairs of them in the 3 ways in which such pairs can be
chosen, such as the rows, columns, and letters of the
square. Similarly, the 8 independent contrasts among
9 objects can be resolved into 4 independent sets of

2 degrees of freedom each, found by dividing the whole into 3 sets of 3 objects. This comes from the fact that not only is a 3×3 Latin square possible, but a 3×3 Græco-Latin square. A pair of letters, one Greek and one Latin, may be assigned to each cell of the square, so that each Latin letter appears once in each row and in each column, and each Greek letter appears once in each row, once in each column, and once with each Latin letter, as is shown below :—

$$
\begin{array}{ccc}
A\alpha & B\beta & C\gamma \\
B\gamma & C\alpha & A\beta \\
C\beta & A\gamma & B\alpha
\end{array}
$$

By rearranging the rows among themselves and also the columns, so that the letters in the first row and in the first column are in order, any Latin square can be reduced to a standard form. Since, after rearranging the columns so that A is on the left of the first row, only the remaining rows will be disturbed, each square of the standard form is capable of generating $s!(s-1)!$ different squares, where s is the number of letters in each row or column. When s is 2 or 3 there is only one solution in the standard position, so that the total numbers of Latin squares are 2 and 12 respectively. There is also essentially only one 3×3 Græco-Latin square, namely that shown above; but apart from the re-arrangement of the Latin letters in the rows and columns in 12 ways, the Greek letters may be permuted among themselves in 6 ways, making 72 arrangements in all.

With 4×4 squares there are four arrangements of the Latin letters in the standard position, or $4 \times 6 \times 24 = 576$ Latin squares. Only one of these 4, however, yields a Græco-Latin square, and that in two ways, so that there are $2 \times 6 \times 24^2$ ($=6912$) 4×4 Græco-Latin squares. The two arrangements of the Greek letters are, moreover, themselves orthogonal, so that the 15 degrees of freedom among 16 objects may be divided into 5 independent sets of 3 each, being the 3 independent comparisons among 4 sets of 4 objects each, into which the whole may be divided. An arrangement of this kind is shown below, in which numeral suffices are used in place of one set of Greek letters :—

$$
\begin{array}{cccc}
A_1a & B_2\beta & C_3\gamma & D_4\delta \\
B_4\gamma & A_3\delta & D_2a & C_1\beta \\
C_2\delta & D_1\gamma & A_4\beta & B_3a \\
D_3\beta & C_4a & B_1\delta & A_2\gamma
\end{array}
$$

There are in all $2 \times 6 \times 24^3$ such arrangements.

The 5×5 Latin squares in the standard position are 56 in number, and fall into two sets. One set of 50 yields no Græco-Latin square, but the set of 6, which are symmetrical about the diagonal, yield each 3 different squares which do not differ merely in a permutation of the Greek letters. There are therefore $3 \times 6 \times 24 \times 120^2$ 5×5 Græco-Latin squares. The three different arrangements are all mutually orthogonal, so that we may add a numeral suffix, as in the 4×4 square above, and obtain $6 \times 6 \times 24 \times 120^3$ solutions. And we may add a second suffix independent of the first, and of the letters, in $6 \times 6 \times 24 \times 120^4$ different ways. An example using two suffices is shown below :—

$$
\begin{array}{ccccc}
A_1a_1 & B_2\beta_2 & C_3\gamma_3 & D_4\delta_4 & E_5\epsilon_5 \\
B_3\delta_5 & C_4\epsilon_1 & D_5a_2 & E_1\beta_3 & A_2\gamma_4 \\
C_5\beta_4 & D_1\gamma_5 & E_2\delta_1 & A_3\epsilon_2 & B_4a_3 \\
D_2\epsilon_3 & E_3a_4 & A_4\beta_5 & B_5\gamma_1 & C_1\delta_2 \\
E_4\gamma_2 & A_5\delta_3 & B_1\epsilon_4 & C_2a_5 & D_3\beta_1
\end{array}
$$

Consequently, the 24 degrees of freedom among 25 objects can be subdivided into 6 independent sets of 4 corresponding to the rows, columns, Latin letters, first suffices, Greek letters and second suffices in the square above. Such a square may be said to be completely orthogonal.

Completely Orthogonal 8×8 Square

```
1 1     2 5     3 2     4 3     5 7     6 4     7 8     8 6
1 1 1   7 3 8   5 4 7   2 6 5   8 2 6   3 8 2   6 5 4   4 7 3
1 1     4 6     6 8     8 7     3 4     7 5     2 3     5 2

2 2     1 8     7 1     6 7     8 3     4 6     3 5     5 4
2 2 2   3 7 5   8 6 3   1 4 8   5 1 4   7 5 1   4 8 6   6 3 7
2 2     6 4     4 5     5 3     7 6     3 8     1 7     8 1

3 3     7 4     1 7     5 1     4 2     8 5     2 6     6 8
3 3 3   2 1 6   4 5 2   7 8 4   6 7 8   1 6 7   8 4 5   5 2 1
3 3     5 8     8 6     6 2     1 5     2 4     7 1     4 7

4 4     6 3     5 6     1 5     3 8     2 1     8 7     7 2
4 4 4   8 5 7   3 1 8   6 2 3   7 6 2   5 7 6   2 3 1   1 8 5
4 4     1 2     2 7     7 8     5 1     8 3     6 5     3 6

5 5     8 1     4 8     3 4     1 6     7 3     6 2     2 7
5 5 5   6 4 2   1 3 6   8 7 1   2 8 7   4 2 8   7 1 3   3 6 4
5 5     3 7     7 2     2 6     4 3     6 1     8 4     1 8

6 6     4 7     8 4     2 8     7 5     1 2     5 3     3 1
6 6 6   5 8 3   7 2 5   4 1 7   3 4 1   8 3 4   1 7 2   2 5 8
6 6     2 1     1 3     3 5     8 2     5 7     4 8     7 4

7 7     3 6     2 3     8 2     6 1     5 8     1 4     4 5
7 7 7   1 2 4   6 8 1   3 5 6   4 3 5   2 4 3   5 6 8   8 1 2
7 7     8 5     5 4     4 1     2 8     1 6     3 2     6 3

8 8     5 2     6 5     7 6     2 4     3 7     4 1     1 3
8 8 8   4 6 1   2 7 4   5 3 2   1 5 3   6 1 5   3 2 7   7 4 6
8 8     7 3     3 1     1 4     6 7     4 2     5 6     2 5
```

Although there are 9408 6×6 Latin squares in the standard position, belonging to 12 distinct types, yet none of these yields a Græco-Latin square, a conclusion arrived at by Euler after a considerable investigation, but only recently established for certain by the enumeration of the actual types which occur. Græco-Latin squares are easily formed with 7 units in a side, or any other odd number; the 7×7 squares have been enumerated by Norton. It may be shown that with any prime number (p) the $p^2 - 1$ degrees of freedom among p^2 objects may be separated into $p + 1$ independent sets of

F

$p-1$ degrees of freedom each, each representing comparisons among p groups of p objects. Yates has shown that this is also true of 8^2 objects, and the same can be done with 9^2, as the examples illustrate. Stevens has demonstrated the possibility in general for powers of prime numbers.

After the rows and columns, the categories of subdivision are represented by the numbers in the cells of each square. The squares given may be randomised by permuting, (a) the rows, columns, and each set of numbers among themselves, (b) whole sets of numbers with each other and with the rows and columns.

Thus, in the 8×8 square shown above, the seven numbers represent seven different ways of dividing 64 objects into 8 groups of 8 each, making with the rows and columns 9 ways in all, so that no two objects are classified alike in any two of the nine ways.

Completely Orthogonal 9×9 Square

1111	2322	3233	9549	7457	8668	5975	6886	4794
1111	4546	7978	3834	6369	9492	2627	5753	8285
2246	3154	1365	7672	8583	9491	6717	4928	5839
8322	2454	5889	7715	1247	4673	9538	3961	6196
3378	1289	2197	8414	9625	7536	4843	5751	6962
6233	9665	3797	5926	8158	2581	4419	7842	1374
4435	5616	6524	3861	1742	2953	8399	9277	7188
9744	3279	6612	8567	2993	5135	7351	1486	4828
5567	6448	4659	1996	2874	3785	9132	7313	8221
4955	7187	1523	6448	9871	3316	5262	8694	2739
6693	4571	5482	2738	3919	1827	7264	8145	9356
2866	5398	8431	1659	4782	7224	3143	6575	9917
7729	8937	9818	6255	4166	5344	2681	3592	1473
5477	8813	2345	4291	7636	1768	6984	9129	3552
8852	9763	7941	4387	5298	6179	3426	1634	2515
3688	6721	9256	2172	5514	8949	1895	4337	7463
9984	7895	8776	5123	6331	4212	1558	2469	3647
7599	1932	4164	9383	3425	6857	8776	2218	5641

35·01 Configurations in Three or More Dimensions

Instead of considering a square, we may consider a configuration of n^3 elements, arranged in layers of n^2 elements each, there being three sets of such layers intersecting at right angles. Then any two layers of different sets will intersect in n common elements.

The first n letters of the Latin alphabet may be assigned to n^2 elements each, so that n of these fall in each layer of each of these sets. We thus form a Latin cube. If the process were repeated with n letters of the Greek alphabet, with the added restriction that each of the Latin letters coincides n times with each of the Greek letters, we should have a Græco-Latin cube. The greatest possible number of alphabets which can be accommodated in this way is $(n-1)(n+2)$, or n^2+n-2, but so many as this may not be possible for particular values of n. Together with the three modes of subdivision of the elements into n sets of n^2 each provided by the three sets of layers of the cube, the maximum number of modes of subdivision is n^2+n+1.

An elementary proof of this limitation, though somewhat an intricate one, is given below.

Let us suppose that there are q categories each dividing the n^3 elements into n sets of n^2 elements each. Then the number of pairs of elements alike in respect to any one category will be

$$\tfrac{1}{2}n^3(n^2-1),$$

and for all categories the number must be

$$\tfrac{1}{2}qn^3(n^2-1).$$

Now any pair of elements may be alike in respect to a certain number of categories, let us say p, which may differ from one pair to another, and may be zero for some pairs, but in any case we must have the relationship

$$\tfrac{1}{2}qn^3(n^2-1) = \varSigma(p) \, ;$$

where

$$\varSigma(p)$$

stands for the sum of the values of p for all possible pairs.

Further, each pair of categories divides the elements into n^2 sets of n elements each, such that members of the same set are alike in respect of both categories. Hence the total number of pairs alike in both categories is

$$\tfrac{1}{2}n^3(n-1),$$

and, as there are

$$\tfrac{1}{2}q(q-1)$$

pairs of categories in all, the total number of cases in which two elements are alike in two categories is

$$\tfrac{1}{4}q(q-1)n^3(n-1) \, ;$$

but a pair of elements alike in p categories will contribute

$$\tfrac{1}{2}p(p-1)$$

cases to this total.   Hence

$$\tfrac{1}{2}q(q-1)n^3(n-1) = \varSigma(p^2-p).$$

We may now use the inequality

$$\tfrac{1}{2}n^3(n^3-1)\varSigma(p^2) \geqslant \varSigma^2(p),$$

since the number of pairs of elements, each contributing a value of p, is

$$\tfrac{1}{2}n^3(n^3-1) \, ;$$

the limiting equality being realised only when all values of p are equal.

Hence

$$\tfrac{1}{4}q^2n^6(n^2-1)^2 \leqslant \tfrac{1}{4}n^6(n^3-1)(n-1)q(q-1)+\tfrac{1}{4}n^6(n^3-1)(n^2-1)q$$

whence dividing by

$$\tfrac{1}{4}qn^6$$

$$q\{(n^2-1)^2-(n^3-1)(n-1)\} \leqslant (n^3-1)(n^2-n),$$

or

$$n(n-1)^2q \leqslant n(n-1)^2(n^2+n+1)$$

$$q \leqslant n^2+n+1.$$

The largest possible number of categories is therefore

$$n^2+n+1,$$

and, if this number is realised, the number of categories in which any two elements are alike must be constant and equal to

$$\frac{n^2-1}{n^3-1}\,(n^2+n+1) = n+1.$$

If instead of a cube we have a configuration of n^r elements, the form of proof used above leads to the result that the greatest possible number of categories is

$$(n^r-1)/(n-1),$$

and that with this number every pair of elements will be alike in

$$(n^{r-1}-1)/(n-1)$$

different categories.

It is demonstrable that this maximum number can be realised whenever n is a power of a prime. An example of a cube with $n = 3$, in ten alphabets, represented by the ten positions in the triangles, is shown below. The first three letters of each alphabet are represented by o, 1 and 2.

Cube of 3 in Ten Alphabets

```
0000  1111  2222      0012  1120  2201      0021  1102  2210
 000   001   002       121   122   120       212   210   211
  00    21    12        11    02    20        22    10    01
   0     1     2         2     0     1         1     2     0

1200  2011  0122      1212  2020  0101      1221  2002  0110
 111   112   110       202   200   201       020   021   022
 .12    00    21        20    11    02        01    22    10
   1     2     0         0     1     2         2     0     1

2100  0211  1022      2112  0220  1001      2121  0202  1010
 222   220   221       010   011   012       101   102   100
  21    12    00        02    20    11        10    01    22
   2     0     1         1     2     0         0     1     2
```

Such configurations in three or more dimensions greatly facilitate the solution of problems of confounding discussed in sections 35·1 to 47.

35·1. An Exceptional Design

The principal use of Græco-Latin and higher squares consists in clarifying complex combinatorial situations, and will be illustrated in later chapters. Occasionally, however, they may be used directly in experimental design. An example of this exceptional use has been given by L. H. C. Tippett.

In a cotton mill one of 5 spindles was found to be winding defective weft. The cause of the defect was unknown. Its origin could, however, be traced further by interchanging the component parts of the spindle. Four portions could thus be interchanged, designated by the symbols, w, x, y and z.

These parts were reassembled in twenty-five ways, so that each of the five components w was used once in combination with each of the five components x, and so with each pair of components. The reconstructed spindles were tested five at a time, over five periods, so that each component was used equally during each period.

The combinations used and the distribution of defects in the resulting weft are shown in Table 8·1.

TABLE 8·1

Spindle Composition and Defects Observed

Period.	Composition of Spindle.				
1	$w_1x_1y_1z_1$	$w_2x_2y_2z_2$ ++	$w_3x_3y_3z_3$ +	$w_4x_4y_4z_4$	$w_5x_5y_5z_5$
2	$w_1x_5y_4z_3$	$w_2x_1y_5z_4$ ++	$w_3x_2y_1z_5$	$w_4x_3y_2z_1$	$w_5x_4y_3z_2$
3	$w_1x_4y_2z_5$ +	$w_2x_5y_3z_1$ +|+	$w_3x_1y_4z_2$	$w_4x_2y_5z_3$	$w_5x_3y_1z_4$
4	$w_1x_3y_5z_2$	$w_2x_4y_1z_3$ ++	$w_3x_5y_2z_4$	$w_4x_1y_3z_5$	$w_5x_2y_4z_1$
5	$w_1x_2y_3z_4$ +	$w_2x_3y_4z_5$ ++	$w_3x_4y_5z_1$	$w_4x_5y_1z_2$ +	$w_5x_1y_2z_3$

In the table moderate defect is marked +, and severe defect ++. It will be seen that severe defect is confined to the five spindles made up using the component w_2, and is invariably present when this component is used. The origin of the trouble was therefore traced to this part, and this knowledge led to the discovery of a cause of defect previously unsuspected.

Of the remaining 20 bobbins, 4 showed defect to a moderate degree. There is no sufficient reason to ascribe this partial failure to the parts used; the only parts which show defect more than once are w_1 and y_3.

In general, the danger of trying to test five different factors (the four components and the period) each susceptible of five variants, in only 25 trials, lies in the fact that we are examining only 25, out of 3125 possible

combinations. In consequence any interactions between
the effects of one component and those of another may
appear in the results as due to a third component. The
value of the test for its special purpose arises from the
technologist's assurance that such consistent interaction
is, in the special circumstances, very improbable. He
has, therefore, confidence in interpreting Table 8·1 as
condemning the component w_2. A theorist without
such practical knowledge would, however, have no
difficulty in accounting for the effect in terms of x, y
and z, and without taking account of w. For example,
if in the table we add the suffices of x and y and subtract
that of z, severe defect is only found when the resulting
number is 2 or 7, and is then invariably found. Such
a result might be actually misleading if the suffices
represented quantitative physical attributes of the components, and had not been assigned arbitrarily by the
experimenter.

36. Practical Exercises

For experimental purposes it is, of course, the
properties of the smaller squares that are most useful.
The following data supply an example for readers who
wish to familiarise themselves with the analysis of
variance in its application to experiments designed in a
Latin square. They represent the results of such an
experiment carried out in potatoes at Ely in 1932. The
six treatments designated by A B C D E F consist
of different quantities of nitrogenous and phosphatic
fertilisers. The results in lbs. of potatoes are quoted,
with some simplification, from the 1932 Report of
Rothamsted Experimental Station. The analysis may
be checked by comparison with Tables 31 and 32.

TABLE 9

Arrangement and Yields of a Latin Square

E 633	B 527	F 652	A 390	C 504	D 416	3122
B 489	C 475	D 415	E 488	F 571	A 282	2720
A 384	E 481	C 483	B 422	D 334	F 646	2750
F 620	D 448	E 505	C 439	A 323	B 384	2719
D 452	A 432	B 411	F 617	E 594	C 466	2972
C 500	F 505	A 259	D 366	B 326	E 420	2376
3078	2868	2725	2722	2652	2614	16659

The following puzzle is of service in familiar-ising the mind with the combinatorial relationships underlying the use of the Latin square, and the like, in experimental design :—

Sixteen passengers on a liner discover that they are an exceptionally representative body. Four are Englishmen, four are Scots, four are Irish, and four are Welsh. There are also four each of four different ages, 35, 45, 55 and 65, and no two of the same age are of the same nationality. By profession also four are lawyers, four soldiers, four doctors and four clergy-men, and no two of the same profession are of the same age or of the same nationality. It appears, also, that four are bachelors, four married, four widowed and four divorced, and that no two of the same marital status are of the same profession, or the same age, or the same nationality. Finally, four are conservatives, four liberals, four socialists and four fascists, and no two of the same political sympathies are of the same marital status, or the same profession, or the same age, or the same nationality.

Three of the fascists are known to be an unmarried English lawyer of 65, a married Scots soldier of 55 and a widowed Irish doctor of 45. It is then easy to specify the remaining fascist.

It is further given that the Irish socialist is 35, the conservative of 45 is a Scotsman, and the Englishman of 55 is a clergyman. What do you know of the Welsh lawyer?

REFERENCES AND OTHER READING

Rothamsted Experimental Station Annual Report (1932).

R. A. FISHER (1925-48). Statistical methods for research workers. Chap. VIII., § 49.

R. A. FISHER and F. YATES (1934). The 6×6 Latin squares. Proceedings of the Cambridge Philosophical Society, xxx. 492-507.

W. L. STEVENS (1939). The completely orthogonalised Latin square. Annals of Eugenics, ix. 82-93.

O. TEDIN (1931). The influence of systematic plot arrangement upon the estimate of error in field experiments. Journal of Agricultural Science, xxi. 191-208.

L. H. C. TIPPETT (1934). Applications of statistical methods to the control of quality in industrial production. Manchester Statistical Society.

H. W. NORTON (1939). The 7×7 squares. Annals of Eugenics, ix. 269-307.

VI

THE FACTORIAL DESIGN IN EXPERIMENTATION

37. The Single Factor

In expositions of the scientific use of experimentation it is frequent to find an excessive stress laid on the importance of varying the essential conditions *only one at a time*. The experimenter interested in the causes which contribute to a certain effect is supposed, by a process of abstraction, to isolate these causes into a number of elementary ingredients, or factors, and it is often supposed, at least for purposes of exposition, that to establish controlled conditions in which all of these factors except one can be held constant, and then to study the effects of this single factor, is the essentially scientific approach to an experimental investigation. This ideal doctrine seems to be more nearly related to expositions of elementary physical theory than to laboratory practice in any branch of research. In experiments merely designed to illustrate or demonstrate simple laws, connecting cause and effect, the relationships of which with the laws relating to other causes are already known, it provides a means by which the student may apprehend the relationship, with which he is to familiarise himself, in as simple a manner as possible. By contrast, in the state of knowledge or ignorance in which genuine research, intended to advance knowledge, has to be carried on, this simple formula is not very helpful. We are usually ignorant which, out of innumerable possible factors, may prove ultimately to be the most important, though we may have strong presuppositions that some few of them are particularly worthy of study. We have usually no knowledge that any one factor will exert its effects independently of all others that can be varied, or that its effects are particularly simply related to variations in these other factors. On the contrary, when factors are chosen for investigation, it is not because we anticipate that the laws of nature can be expressed with any particular simplicity in terms of these variables, but because they are variables which can be controlled or measured with comparative ease. If the investigator, in these circumstances, confines his attention to any single factor, we may infer either that he is the unfortunate victim of a doctrinaire theory as to how experimentation should proceed, or that the time, material or equipment at his disposal is too limited to allow him to give attention to more than one narrow aspect of his problem.

The modifications possible to any complicated apparatus, machine or industrial process must always be considered as potentially interacting with one another, and must be judged by the probable effects of such interactions. If they have to be tested one at a time this is not because to do so is an ideal scientific procedure, but because to test them simultaneously would sometimes be too troublesome, or too costly. In many instances, as will be shown in this chapter, the belief that this is so has little foundation. Indeed, in a wide class of cases an experimental investigation, at the same time as it is made more comprehensive, may also be made more efficient if by more efficient we mean that more knowledge and a higher degree of precision are obtainable by the same number of observations.

38. A Simple Factorial Scheme

As an example, let us consider the case in which we require to study experimentally the effects of variations in composition of a mixture containing four active ingredients. It is indifferent for our illustration for what purpose the mixture may be required. It may be an industrial product, a medicinal prescription, a food ration or an artificial manure. It is sufficient that its efficacy in practical use cannot be calculated *a priori*, but can be measured by its effect in particular trials ; and that the ideal quantitative composition is unknown in respect to all four ingredients. In principle, it matters little whether our doubts extend to wide variations in the quantities to be employed, or whether the variations in question are proportionately small ; as they will be when wide experience has already determined the ideal proportions within narrow limits. Nor will it affect the question in principle, if, as in some cases, the cost of the items is an important consideration to be debited in assessing the net advantage of using more of them ; or whether, as in other cases, the direct observations or measurements made in the test are alone to be considered.

So defined, the situation is clearly one of very wide occurrence. Let us consider an experiment in which 16 different mixtures are made up in the 16 combinations possible by combining either a larger or a smaller quantity of each of the 4 ingredients to be tested. The quantities may differ in some cases by a factor as large as 2, in which case each mixture will contain of each ingredient either a single or a double quantity. The factor need not be the same for all ingredients. For some one or more of them we may doubt whether its presence in any quantity is desirable ; or whether it had not better be omitted altogether. We shall then test mixtures with or without this component. But, in any case, the general question as to whether, of each ingredient, more or less can be added with advantage, can be settled by making up all combinations, using either more or less of each component.

We will suppose now that 6 tests are made with each mixture, or 96 in all. The particular cases in which the different mixtures are to be tried will be assigned strictly at random ; or, as in the agricultural experiment illustrated in Chapter IV. (randomised blocks), the tests will be divided into 6 series, each supposedly more homogeneous than the whole, and the 16 members of each will be assigned at random to different mixtures. Since no difference of principle arises here we will at first suppose that the tests are assigned entirely at random.

In respect of any one particular ingredient the first point to be noted is that we have for comparison 48 cases in which a larger, and 48 in which a smaller quantity has been employed. These 48 are not all alike in other respects. They are alike in sets of 6, but the eight sets differ from each other in the other ingredients used. Corresponding to each set of 6 in which a larger quantity of the first ingredient has been used, there will, however, be a set of 6 with a smaller quantity, and exactly similar to it in respect of the other ingredients. The difference, if any, in the effects observed in these two sets must be ascribed, apart from random fluctuations, to the particular ingredient in which they differ. Moreover, there are 8 such pairs of sets to supply confirmatory evidence of this effect if it exists. For each single factor, therefore, we have a direct comparison of the averages or totals of two sets of 48 trials ; and this comparison will have the same precision as if the whole of the 96 trials had been devoted to testing the efficacy of one single component. The first fact contributing to the efficiency of experiments designed on the factorial system, is that every trial supplies information upon each of the main questions which the experiment is designed to examine.

The advantage of the factorial arrangement over a series of experiments, each designed to test a single factor is, however, much greater than this. For with separate experiments we should obtain no light whatever on the possible interactions of the different ingredients, even if we had gone to the labour of performing 96 experiments with each of them, and so, for each singly, had attained the same precision as that which the factorial experiment can give. If, for example, an increase in ingredient A were advantageous in the presence of B, but were ineffective or disadvantageous in its absence, we could only hope to learn this fact by carrying out our test of A both in the presence and in the absence of B ; and this, in fact, is what the factorial experiment is designed to do—but to do so thoroughly that the total system of possible interactions is explored in its entirety. To test if the effect of A in the presence of B is greater than in its absence, we may compare the total difference ascribable to A from one set of 24 pairs of otherwise comparable trials, in all of which B is present, with the corresponding effect derived from the remaining pair of sets of 24, in all of which B is absent. This is the same as comparing the results of 48 trials in which A and B are both employed in large, or both in small, quantity, with the other 48 trials in which the larger quantity of A and the smaller quantity of B, or *vice versâ*, have been combined. We have thus again a comparison between the results of two sets of 48 trials, comparable in all other respects save that in which we are interested, namely, whether the effect of an increase in A is, or is not, influenced by an increase in B. This difference, if it exists, might equally be expressed by saying that an increase in B is influenced in its effect by an increase in A. The difference, in fact, involves the two ingredients symmetrically, and is technically spoken of as the interaction of A with B. There are clearly 6 such interactions between pairs of the 4 ingredients, and each of these is evaluated by the experiment with the same precision.

The 4 contrasts for single ingredients, and the 6 interactions between pairs of them, still do not exhaust the possible interactions which may be present, and which the experiment is competent to reveal. It might be, for example, that the interaction between A and B is itself influenced by the quantity of the ingredient C. If we were to calculate the interaction of A and B for those mixtures which had a larger quantity of C, and subtract from this the corresponding interaction for mixtures having the smaller quantity of C, we should, in fact, be adding up all the results from mixtures having either all three or any one of the ingredients A, B and C present in the larger quantity, and subtracting from this total the effects of all the mixtures having either none or any two. The measure of discrepancy is, therefore, symmetrically related to the three ingredients A, B and C, and is known as the interaction of these three ingredients. If such an interaction exists the fact may be stated, as above, by saying that the interaction of A and B depends on the quantity of C present. Equally, we might make the equivalent statement that the interaction of B and C depends on the quantity of A present, or that the interaction of C and A depends on the quantity of B. The three statements are logically equivalent ; and for any set of three ingredients there will be only one numerical measure of the interaction

to be ascertained from the data. Since there are four
sets of three which we might choose, there are four
triple interactions which can be evaluated, each of which,
like the interactions between two ingredients, is found
by the comparison of a set of 48 chosen tests, with
another set of 48 in other respects comparable with it.

Finally, if we ask whether the interaction of A, B
and C is dependent on the quantity of D present, it
appears that the answer to our question must be a
comparison symmetrically related to all four ingredients.
This is made by comparing the effects of those mixtures
in which there is a larger quantity of 4, 2 or none of
the ingredients with the effects of those mixtures in
which there is a larger quantity of 3 or 1 of them. There
is thus only one quadruple interaction in the system,
and this will be evaluated with the same precision as
all the others. We thus find that the 15 independent
comparisons among the 16 different mixtures, which
have been made up, may be logically resolved into
15 intelligible components, as shown in the following
table :—

TABLE 10

Effects of single ingredients .	. .	4
Interactions of 2 ,,	. . .	6
,, ,, 3 ,,	. . .	4
,, ,, 4 ,,	. . .	1
	Total .	15

The numbers are the coefficients of the binomial expansion $(1+x)^4$, omitting the first. Each particular interaction may be clearly designated by the selection of
letters, such as ABC, which represent the ingredients
contributing to it. With respect to sign, it is a convenient
convention to speak of an interaction as positive when
the measured effects of the set of mixtures which

G

contain all the ingredients involved in larger quantity exceed the measured effects of the remaining set.

The second advantage which we may note, therefore, in a factorially arranged experiment is that, in addition to measuring the effects of the four single ingredients with the same precision as though the whole of the experiment had been devoted to each of them, it measures also the 11 possible interactions between these ingredients with the same precision. These interactions may, or may not, be considerable in magnitude. It is none the less of importance in practical cases to know whether they are considerable or not.

The precision with which the 15 comparisons have been made is, of course, estimated from the variation between the results of the 6 trials of each mixture. Each mixture will therefore provide 5 degrees of freedom for making a pooled estimate of the precision of the experiment, thus giving 80 degrees of freedom in all. The analysis of variance of the 96 trials thus takes the simple form :—

TABLE 11

	Degrees of Freedom.
Treatments . . .	15
Error	80
Total .	95

The sum of squares corresponding to error is divided by 80 to obtain the estimated variance of a single experiment. This, multiplied by 96, gives the estimated variance of the difference between the sum of any chosen set of 48 results and the sum of the remainder. Thus we have only to add one-fifth of its value to the sum of squares for error, and take the square root, to find the standard deviation appropriate to each of the

15 comparisons that have been made, and in relation
to which the significance of each may be judged. Since
80 is a relatively ample number of degrees of freedom
for the estimation of error, those differences may conveniently be judged significant, which exceed twice
their standard errors.

Had the experiment been arranged, for greater
precision, in 6 blocks of trials, we should in the analysis
eliminate the differences between these blocks from the
estimate of error.   We should then have :—

TABLE 12

			Degrees of Freedom.
Blocks	.	. . .	5
Treatments		. . .	15
Error	.	. . .	75
	Total	.	95

leaving 75 degrees of freedom for the estimation of
error ; so that the sum of squares for error must be
multiplied by 96/75 or 1·28 to obtain the variance
of any comparison between 48 chosen tests and the
remaining 48.

39. The Basis of Inductive Inference

We have seen that the factorial arrangement possesses
two advantages over experiments involving only single
factors : (i) Greater *efficiency*, in that these factors are
evaluated with the same precision by means of only a
quarter of the number of observations that would
otherwise be necessary ; and (ii) Greater *comprehensiveness* in that, in addition to the 4 effects of single factors,
their 11 possible interactions are evaluated.   There is
a third advantage which, while less obvious than the
former two, has an important bearing upon the utility
of the experimental results in their practical application.

This is that any conclusion, such as that it is advantageous to increase the quantity of a given ingredient, has a wider inductive basis when inferred from an experiment in which the quantities of other ingredients have been varied, than it would have from any amount of experimentation, in which these had been kept strictly constant. The exact standardisation of experimental conditions, which is often thoughtlessly advocated as a panacea, always carries with it the real disadvantage that a highly standardised experiment supplies direct information only in respect of the narrow range of conditions achieved by standardisation. Standardisation, therefore, weakens rather than strengthens our ground for inferring a like result, when, as is invariably the case in practice, these conditions are somewhat varied. As the analysis of variance clearly shows, such standardisation of conditions is only of value in increasing the precision of the experimental data when it is applied to the tests to be compared experimentally, differences between which affect the real errors, and the estimates of error with which they are randomised. Such standardisation is out of place when applied to parallel tests designed, by multiplying the observations, to increase the precision of all comparisons. In fact, as the factorial arrangement well illustrates, we may, by deliberately varying in each case some of the conditions of the experiment, achieve a wider inductive basis for our conclusions, without in any degree impairing their precision.

40. Inclusion of Subsidiary Factors

Factorial types of arrangement, by reconciling the desiderata of a relatively wide exploration with high precision, without sacrifice of either advantage, are eminently suitable when alternative procedures of any kind are apparently open to the experimenter. Thus it may be doubtful whether the cultivation of an orchard is most advantageously carried out in the spring or the autumn of the year. More than one method of cultivation, also, may be advocated with apparently equal force. Numerous similar examples will occur when the modification of any practical procedure is under consideration. Schools of opinion are formed on points which without systematic trial we cannot know to have, or to lack, real importance, as bee-keepers dispute whether the combs should lie parallel from the front of the hive to the back, or should lie transversely to this direction. These are all qualitative differences, but, provided that there is a quantitative method of measuring any real advantage which they may confer, they may be incorporated in experiments designed primarily to test other points ; with the real advantages that, if either general effects or interactions are detected, that will be so much knowledge gained at no expense to the other objects of the experiment ; and that, in any case, there will be no reason for rejecting the experimental results on the ground that the test was made in conditions differing in one or other of these respects from those in which it is proposed to apply the results.

There is another feature widespread in experimental work where the factorial arrangement relieves the investigator of a troublesome cause of anxiety ; namely, that the isolation of a single factor for separate experimentation can often be achieved only at the expense of a somewhat questionable arbitrariness of definition. To consider a very simple case, the experimenter may undertake to test the respective yields of two or more varieties of a cereal crop. At first sight it will readily be admitted that all other factors likely to affect the yield shall be made the same for the varieties to be compared. So the quantity of seed sown must be equalised. But if the seed-rates are measured in bushels per acre, the bushels, measured as equal volumes of seed of the different varieties, may differ in their weight ; or, again, they may differ even more conspicuously in the numbers of seeds which they contain. If the test is to be carried out at the same single seed-rate for each variety, the equality of seed-rate must be defined, for the purpose of the test, with some degree of arbitrariness. Unless we have assurance that variations in seed-rate will not affect the yield obtained, this arbitrariness will infect the results of the experiment. Clearly, on the question at issue, as between the varieties, it would be desirable to make a comparison using for each variety that seed-rate which is most profitable for it. This may differ from equality, as measured by volume or by weight, or by number of seeds to the acre, by reason of the different capacities of the varieties to withstand causes of death, or, by forming additional shoots, to fill up vacant spaces. The experimenter who, in testing the varieties, at the same time makes a sufficient variation in seed-rates to embrace the optimal value, is clearly in a better position to meet the criticisms which may arise from these considerations, than is one who adopts any arbitrary conventions as to what the phrase " equality of conditions " is intended to convey.

In the conditions of cereal cultivation, moreover, variations in seed-rate inevitably raise with them further questions. In particular, what space should be left between the seed-rows or drills ? At a heavier seed-rate it is reasonable to suppose that the drills could with advantage be placed nearer together than they could if less corn were sown. Consequently, the question as to what is the most advantageous seed-rate can never be answered experimentally without a simultaneous variation in the width of the drills. Equally, no

investigation of the question of drill-width can be satisfactory unless the amount of seed sown be also varied.
The simple question, therefore, of the comparison of the
yields of different varieties of the same crop carries
with it the simultaneous investigation of the effects of
variations in other items of agricultural procedure.
These do not, however, if a logical and comprehensive
plan of experimentation be adopted, add to the cost or
labour of an effective experimental programme. For
extensive replication of the plots sown is in any case
a necessity, if accurate results are to be attained ; and
this replication, at the same time as it increases the
precision of comparisons, may be used simultaneously
to supply the desired variations in all conditions likely
to be bound up with that which is the primary object
of the investigation.

For a given number of trials, the more experimental
variants are tried the fewer will be the absolute replicates.
Thus, with 96 trials, we may have 6 absolute replicates
of 16 different experimental variants, and these, as we
have seen, will still leave 80 degrees of freedom for the
estimation of error. With the same material we might
test 48 different mixtures, or treatments, and still have
duplicate results for each. There would then be 48
degrees of freedom left for error. Although each test
is only made in duplicate, yet all the primary questions,
into which the differences among them may be resolved,
are answered with the same precision as though the
whole experiment had been devoted to each of these
questions alone ; the loss of absolute replication is
made good by the hidden replication inherent in the
factorial arrangement. The experimental error is no
larger, although, being based on only 48 independent
comparisons, it is known with a slightly lower precision
than if 80 had been available. With factorial experi-

ments designed to make a large number of comparisons, there will, in fact, usually be an ample number of degrees of freedom for the estimation of error.

41. Experiments without Replication

It may occasionally be desirable to dispense with absolute replication altogether. This occurs when it is required to test a large number of combinations simultaneously without enlarging the experiment so greatly as to make repeated use of each combination ; and especially, when there is reason to believe that most of the interactions involving 3 or more factors will be unimportant experimentally, in the sense that their real effects, if any, will be too small to be statistically significant, in an experiment of the size contemplated. In such cases the whole of the independent comparisons which the experiment provides may be assigned to the factors tested and their interactions. There will in fact be none ascribable to pure error, but there will be numerous interactions the apparent effects of which are principally due to error, and these may be used to provide a measure of the precision of the more important comparisons.

For example, we may have 6 factors each providing two alternatives to be tested ; and though we do not know *a priori* that these factors are unrelated, we may have reason to think that their action should be sufficiently nearly independent for all but the simple interactions between pairs of them to be experimentally negligible. If each of the combinations be tried once, the 63 independent comparisons which the experiment provides may be analysed as in the following table.

TABLE 13

			Degrees of Freedom.
Single factors			6
Interaction between 2 factors . .			15
,, ,, 3 ,, . .			20
,, ,, 4 ,, . .			15
,, ,, 5 ,, . .			6
,, ,, 6 ,, . .			1

Error 42

The 6 primary effects of the individual factors will each be determined, as we have seen, by the whole weight of the evidence of 64 trials. To test the significance of the differences observed, we may use the 42 degrees of freedom for interactions involving more than 2 factors to supply an estimate of error; that is, an estimate of the variance, due to error, of a single trial. The same test may be applied to any of the 15 interactions between pairs of factors which may seem to be possibly significant. If none of these are very important compared with the average of the remainder we have an empirical confirmation of the supposition upon which the experiment was designed, that the 6 primary factors are not strongly related. If, however, contrary to expectation, it appeared that there was a large interaction between two of these factors, it would be advisable to examine separately the interactions between 3 factors which involve these two. We should thus pick out 4 particular suspects out of the 42 degrees of freedom provisionally ascribed to error, leaving 38 in comparison with which their significance could be tested.

Such a plan could, of course, fail; and would do so if a large number of the high order interactions were more important than the primary effects. It would, however, not likely be tried in these circumstances. More frequently we should find that the true error had been but slightly inflated, and the effective precision of the experiment slightly reduced, by the inclusion in the estimate of error of some small components really due to interactions of the factors tested.

REFERENCES AND OTHER READING

R. A. FISHER (1926). The arrangement of field experiments. Journal of Ministry of Agriculture, xxxiii. 503-513.

T. EDEN and R. A. FISHER (1927). The experimental determination of the value of top dressings with cereals. Journal of Agricultural Science, xvii. 548-562.

VII

CONFOUNDING

42. The Problem of Controlling Heterogeneity

IT has been shown in the last chapter that great advantages may be obtained by testing experimentally an aggregate of variants, systematically arranged on the factorial scheme. The illustrations have shown that such aggregates may be very numerous. When, in Chapters III. and IV., the advantages of pairing, or of grouping, the material in relatively homogeneous blocks was discussed, it was seen that the precision attainable by a given amount of experimentation was liable to be reduced, when the number of comparisons to be made was large, by reason of the increased heterogeneity, which must in practice then be permitted, among the tests in the same group.

In agricultural experimentation this effect expresses itself very simply in the increased size of the blocks of land, each of which is to contain plots representative of all the different combinations to be tested. Thus if there are 48 different combinations, each block will have to be nearly an acre in extent, and it is common experience that within so large an area considerably greater soil heterogeneity will be found, than would be the case if the blocks could be reduced in size to a quarter of an acre or less. The same consideration applies to experimentation of all kinds. If large quantities of material are needed, or large numbers of laboratory animals, these will almost invariably be more heterogeneous than smaller lots could be made to be. In like manner, extensive compilations of statistical material often show evidence of such heterogeneity among the several parts which have been assembled, and are seriously injured in value if this heterogeneity is overlooked in making the compilation.

In many fields of experimentation quantitative knowledge is lacking as to the degree of heterogeneity to be anticipated in batches of material of different size, or drawn from more or less diverse sources. This is a drawback to precise planning, which increased care in experimental design will doubtless steadily remove. While, therefore, greater heterogeneity is always, on general principles, to be anticipated, when the scope of an experimental investigation is to be enlarged, this feature will often do but little to annul the advantages discussed in the last chapter. Nevertheless, the means by which such heterogeneity can be controlled are widely applicable, and will generally give a further increase in precision. In agricultural field trials, where the study of heterogeneity has been itself the object of a great deal of deliberate investigation, it is certain that the further advantages to be gained are very considerable.

In the last chapter, we have seen that a factorially arranged experiment supplies information on a large number of experimental comparisons. Some of these, such as the effects of single factors, will always be of interest. It is seldom, too, that we should be willing to forgo knowledge of any interactions which may exist between pairs of these factors. But, in the case of interactions involving 3 factors or more, the position is often somewhat different. Such interactions may with reason be deemed of little experimental value, either because the experimenter is confident that they are quantitatively unimportant, or because, if they were known to exist, there would be no immediate prospect of the fact being utilised. In such cases we may usefully adopt the artifice known as " confounding." This consists of increasing the number of blocks, or groups of relatively homogeneous material, beyond the number of replications in the experiment, so that each replication occupies two or more blocks ; and, at the same time, of arranging that the experimental contrasts between the different blocks within each replication shall be contrasts between unimportant interactions, the study of which the experimenter is willing to sacrifice for the sake of increasing the precision of the remaining contrasts, in which he is specially interested. To do this it must be possible to evaluate these remaining contrasts solely by comparisons within the blocks. It is not necessary, however, that comparisons within any one block should provide the required contrast, but only that it should be possible to build this up by comparisons within all the blocks of a replication.

43. Example with 8 Treatments, Notation

A very simple example of confounding suggests itself when we have 3 factors, of only 2 variants each, and unite them in an experiment involving the 8 combinations, which they provide. It was in such an experiment that the principle of confounding was first used. As a convenient notation for these cases we may call the 3 factors A, B and C. Let us choose to regard one of these 8 variants as a standard, or " control," and denote it by the symbol (1). The variant which differs from this only in the factor A we will denote by (*a*), likewise (*b*) and (*c*) will stand for the two other treatments which differ from the control in respect of the factors B and C. The remaining treatments will differ from the control in either two, or in all three of

the factors used, and may therefore be denoted un-
equivocally by the symbols (ab), (ac), (bc) and (abc).
The same symbols may be used for the treatments,
and for the quantitative measures of the results of these
treatments, which the experiment is designed to ascertain.
Thus (ab) will stand either for a particular treatment
applied to an agricultural crop, or to the total yield of
the plots which have received this treatment. Equally,
it might be the average live weight, or the average
longevity, of experimental animals which have been
treated in this way, if the experiment is aimed at studying
the conditions which influence weight or longevity.

In contradistinction to the treatments, or experimental variants, denoted by such symbols as (a) we
shall use A, B, etc., to denote the experimental contrasts
found for the factors, and for their interactions. Thus
A will stand for the factor A and for its effect as measured
by summing the treatments the symbols of which contain
a, and deducting those which do not ; *i.e.*

$$A = (abc)+(ab)+(ac)+(a)-(bc)-(b)-(c)-(1),$$

or, by analogy with the rules of multiplication of
algebraic quantities,

$$A = (a-1)(b+1)(c+1).$$

Similarly,

$$B = (b-1)(a+1)(c+1),$$

and

$$C = (c-1)(a+1)(b+1).$$

The corresponding expressions for the interactions
between pairs of factors are then easily seen to be

$$AB = (a-1)(b-1)(c+1),$$

$$BC = (b-1)(c-1)(a+1),$$

and

$$CA = (c-1)(a-1)(b+1).$$

Finally, the interaction of all 3 factors has the symbolic
expression

$$ABC = (a-1)(b-1)(c-1).$$

The purpose of the symbolism is to make it easy to denote any particular contrast, or interaction, and to ascertain at once how the treatments should be compounded in evaluating it.

44. Design suited to Confounding the Triple Interaction

Such a set of eight treatments might be not inconveniently tested in groups of eight experimental trials, on relatively homogeneous material, or on blocks of land, each containing 8 plots. If, however, we decide in advance that the whole value of the experiment lies in the simple contrasts A, B, C, and in the interactions between pairs of factors, AB, BC, and CA, while the interaction between all 3 factors, ABC, is unimportant and may be neglected, then it is possible to divide the land into blocks of only four plots each, or, in general, to subdivide the experimental material in groups of four, choosing thus more homogeneous groups than could be obtained if 8 had to be included in each group. To do this we notice that the particular interaction ABC, which we are willing to sacrifice, is a simple contrast between one particular four of our eight treatments, namely,

$$(abc)+(a)+(b)+(c),$$

and the remaining four

$$(ab)+(bc)+(ca)+(1),$$

as in Fig. 1.

(c)	(bc)
(abc)	(ab)
(a)	(1)
(b)	(ac)

FIG. 1.—Diagram showing the arrangement of eight treatments in two complementary blocks belonging to the same replication.

If, therefore, these sets of four treatments are grouped together in blocks, and two such blocks be assigned to each replication, the contrast between the blocks within each replication is merely the treatment contrast which we are willing to sacrifice. This contrast has, therefore, been confounded indistinguishably with the differences between blocks, which are intended to be eliminated from the experimental errors of the comparisons we wish to make, and from the estimate of these errors. The remaining contrasts, representing single factors, or interactions between pairs of them, though none of them can be made by comparisons within a single block, are all built up by combining a contrast of one pair of treatments and another in the same block, with a similar contrast inside the other block of the replication. The reader should satisfy himself that this is so by examining each of these contrasts. It is then apparent that the errors to which these contrasts are subject arise solely from heterogeneity within the sets of four trials constituting the blocks, and that the differences between different blocks contribute nothing to the experimental error. By confounding the one unimportant contrast with the differences between blocks, it is therefore possible to evaluate the six more important contrasts with whatever added precision is attained by using more homogeneous material.

45. Effect on Analysis of Variance

As an example, let us suppose such a test were carried out with 5 replications. There would then be ten blocks, and 9 degrees of freedom belong to the contrasts between these blocks, which have been eliminated from the experimental error. Of these 9, one may be identified with the treatment contrast which has been confounded. The three independent comparisons, within each of the ten blocks of 4, must be assigned 30 degrees of freedom. Of these, 6 stand for the treatment contrasts evaluated, and the remaining 24 for the experimental error available for estimating the precision of the experiment, and for testing the significance of any particular result. The analysis of any such experiment is, therefore, of the form given below :—

TABLE 14

	Degrees of Freedom.
Blocks	9
Treatments	6
Error	24
Total .	39

It is often instructive, and affords a useful check in more confusing examples, to see how the components ascribable to error may be obtained independently, rather than only by subtraction from the total. In this case there are two sets of five blocks, each containing identical treatments. The three differences among these treatments have, therefore, each been evaluated 5 times, and the 4 discrepancies between these 5 values will give 12 differences due wholly to error. Equally, the other set of five blocks contribute the other 12 degrees of freedom or error, making 24 in all, the total required.

Without confounding, the analysis of the experiment would read :—

TABLE 15

	Degrees of Freedom.
Blocks	4
Treatments	7
Error	28
Total .	39

so that the effect of the subdivision of the replications has been to eliminate 5 additional degrees of freedom,

H

one from the treatments and four from the error. If greater homogeneity has in fact been obtained from the subdivision, the components by which the error has been diminished will have carried away a disproportionate share of the residual variation.

The subdivision of each replication into two or more blocks does not prevent, when this is desired, the isolation, among the degrees of freedom assigned to error, of the particular components of error which affect any chosen comparison within the blocks. Since, however, the comparisons in which we are interested, such as A, are built up of comparisons within blocks of different kinds, they are equally affected by the components of error within each kind of block. Thus, in our present example, instead of 4 degrees of freedom only being available for the estimation of error of the comparison A, 8 are available, and these 8 are the same as affect the precision of the interaction BC. Thus the 24 degrees of freedom for error are divisible into three sets of 8 each, appertaining to three pairs of comparisons among the degrees of freedom ascribed to treatments.

45·1. General Systems of Confounding in Powers of 2

If an experiment involves s factors at two levels each, there will be 2^s different treatments. As in Section 43, any particular treatment may be denoted by a combination of small letters in brackets, and any of the principal comparisons and their interactions by one or more capital letters. Now, just as any two primary comparisons A and B have an interaction AB, so any two comparisons such as ABC and ADE may be regarded as having an interaction. If we divide all the treatments into two halves for the contrast ABC, those in one half, including the control (1), will have an even number of letters in common with ABC, while those in the other half will have an odd number of letters in common with it. The same is true of the cross division of the same treatments into two halves for the comparison ADE. Consequently, if both subdivisions are made at once, the quarter containing the control will contain all treatments having an even number of letters in common both with ABC and with ADE. The opposite quarter will contain all treatments having an odd number of letters in common with both symbols. For this reason, if we combine the two symbols ABC and ADE by throwing them together and deleting any letters they have in common, a process which yields BCDE, this must be a comparison with which the treatments in both these quarters have an even number of letters in common, and is therefore the comparison of these two quarters taken together against the two which are either odd to ABC and even to ADE, or *vice versâ*. The comparison BCDE is thus the interaction of ABC with ADE.

The important consequence of recognising this relationship is that if, in an experiment with many factors, the comparisons ABC and ADE are both confounded, with comparisons between whole blocks, it necessarily follows that BCDE will also be confounded. In the language of the theory of groups, the comparisons confounded (together with an inert symbol I, the "identity") constitute a "subgroup" selected from the "group" constituted by all the comparisons together with the identity. In fact, if we experiment with s factors in blocks of 2^{s-a}, so that there are 2^a blocks in each replication, the $2^s - 1$ comparisons to be made (with the identity) form a group of order 2^s, of which we may choose any subgroup of order 2^a to specify the $2^a - 1$ comparisons to be confounded.

For example, with six factors using four blocks of 16 in each replication, we could not choose as the three comparisons to be confounded the sixfold interaction ABCDEF, and two fivefold interactions, for these would not form a subgroup. The restriction under which the choice is to be made would, however, allow us to use ABC, DEF and their interaction ABCDEF ; or, equally, to use ABCD, CDEF and their interaction ABEF. By this rule the available possibilities may easily be reviewed, and a choice made in accordance with what is known of the factors to be used.

It may be shown that, without confounding any interaction of less than three factors, we may use any number of factors which is less than the number of units in a block. So with blocks of eight we may use up to seven factors, and with blocks of sixteen s may be as large as fifteen.

When only one comparison is confounded, the contents of the two complementary blocks are easily written down. When, however, the subgroup of inter-actions to be confounded is of high order, to arrive at the contents of each block by successive subdivision is a tedious process. The block contents may, however, be written down at once, in the most complicated cases, by another method. It was observed in the first para-graph of this section that the treatment symbols of treatments in the same block with the "control" all have an even number of letters in common with every comparison confounded. (It is sufficient to apply this test to a members of the $2^a - 1$ in the subgroup con-founded, provided these a are all independent, or, in other words, provided they do not belong to a subgroup of the subgroup confounded.) The set of treatment symbols which satisfy this condition themselves form a subgroup, since if any two possess the property, it is obvious that their interaction must do so. Consequently, we have only to find successively $s-a$ such treatment symbols in order to complete the particular block containing the control. This may be called the intrablock subgroup ; it is of order 2^{s-a}. The contents of the block containing any other chosen treatment may then be found by writing down the interactions of this treatment with the treatments of the intrablock subgroup.

For example, to arrange the combinations of 7 factors in blocks of eight, we might choose for confounding first the interaction

ABC ;

if, also, we choose ADE, we write down this new comparison and its interaction with what has gone before, thus :—

ADE, BCDE.

Taking next AFG, we have

AFG, BCFG, DEFG, ABCDEFG ;

BDF has not yet been used, and yields the following eight

BDF, ACDF, ABEF, CEF, ABDG, CDG, BEG, ACEG,

completing the fifteen interactions of the subgroup confounded. For practical purposes we note that any elements from the four lines in which the interactions have been written down constitute a set of four independent generators, from which the whole can be, as indeed it has been, generated. We have now only to find in succession those treatments having an even number of letters in common with each of these four, in order to develop the intrablock subgroup.

It is easy to see that this condition is satisfied, not only by the control (1), but also by

$$(bcde),$$

equally by $(bcfg)$ giving

$$(bcfg), \ (defg) \ ;$$

a third generator is supplied by $(acdf)$ from which we have the last four,

$$(acdf), \ (abef), \ (abdg), \ (aceg)$$

These are, then, the seven treatments in the same block with (1). The contents of the block containing any treatment not in this block may at once be written down from its interactions with these seven.

It will be noticed that in this example the intrablock subgroup is also a subgroup of the subgroup confounded. These two subgroups, each of which can be uniquely derived from the other, may be identical, or one may be a subgroup of the other, or they may have a subgroup in common, or nothing in common but the identity.

In the example in the last section, of three factors in blocks of four, the intrablock subgroup was

$$(1), \ (ab), \ (bc), \ (ac),$$

while the subgroup confounded was

$$I, \ ABC.$$

In order to pass from any satisfactory solution to one involving one factor less, it is a convenient fact that we may delete all symbols of the subgroup confounded which involve any chosen letter, thus halving its order, and at the same time delete the same letter from the symbols in which it occurs in the intrablock subgroup. These changes introduce no new inter-action to be confounded, and do not reduce the order of any, so that if in the initial solution none involves less than three factors, this will still be true of the new solution. Solutions for 6, 5 and 4 factors in blocks of eight may thus be obtained from the solution given above for seven factors.

45·2. Double Confounding

In the Latin square it has been shown possible to eliminate simultaneously the disturbances introduced by heterogeneity of two kinds arising from differences among rows and differences among columns. In the same way a set of 128 tests may be heterogeneous in one respect in blocks of eight, but in another respect in blocks of sixteen, orthogonal to the others. For example, a treatment might be applied at 8 sites on each of 16 cows, with the possibility that the reaction might be affected both by the individuality of the animals and by the differences between the sites chosen. In such cases one subgroup of 15 of the less important interactions could be chosen to be confounded with cows, while a second subgroup, which must have no element in common with the first, could be confounded with sites.

As an illustration, to be worked in detail, if the solution given above were chosen for the distribution of treatment combinations among the different cows, we might choose for confounding with sites the subgroup containing

ABCD,
ABEG, CDEG
BDFG, ACFG, ADEF, BCEF.

To make out a complete scheme showing what

treatment is to be applied at each site on each cow, we must form the intrablock subgroup for sites, namely

$$(efg)$$
$$(cdf), (cdeg)$$
$$(ace), (acfg), (adef), (adg)$$
$$(abf), (abeg), (abcd), (abcdefg), (bcef), (bcg), (bde), (bdfg).$$

These 15 treatments and the control are then assigned to any one site on the 16 cows, and the corresponding treatments at other sites are found from their interactions with the intrablock subgroup for cows. Thus the required treatment at any site may be written out at once in an 8×16 table.

A circumstance well worth taking into account in such cases is that the sites available might be so closely alike in pairs, *e.g.* on the Right and Left sides, that treatments applied at similar sites on the same animal might be regarded as perfectly comparable. On this view only 3 degrees of freedom instead of 7 have been confounded with difference likely to matter, and a set of four interactions, such as the four listed on the last line of the subgroup confounded with sites, will give reliable experimental comparisons. Consequently, we might have used important comparisons, involving only one or two factors, in their place, had this eased the difficulties of setting up a good experimental design.

46. Example with 27 Treatments

The principle of procedure illustrated in Section 44 may be extended and generalised in a large number of ways. Since only a few of these can be exemplified, the reader will find great advantage in investigating the possibilities of similar designs appropriate to the special problems in which he is interested. The variety of the subject is, in fact, unlimited, and probably many valuable possibilities remain to be discovered. We will consider next an experiment with 3 factors, in which each furnishes not two but three variants, so that there are in all 27 combinations to be investigated. Thus a large-scale investigation of the manurial requirements of young rubber plantations, in respect to the three primary manurial elements, nitrogen, potassium and phosphorus, combines, in addition to whatever basal treatment may be thought desirable, single or double applications of these three manures ; making in all three levels for each ingredient, such as nitrogen only, nine combinations for any two ingredients, and 27 for all three together.

In order to reduce the size of the block below that needed to contain 27 plots, we have, to guide us in choosing a smaller size, the fact that blocks of nine will in any case be needed, if all the interactions between pairs of factors are to be conserved. The experiment will therefore have nine plots to a block, and three blocks in each complete replication. Everything now depends on the choice of the sets of nine treatments which are to be assigned to the same blocks, and, of course, within each block to strictly randomised positions. In order to conserve the main effects and the interactions between pairs, a set of nine treatments chosen to occupy the same block must fulfil the following requirements :—

    (i) the three levels of each ingredient must be represented by three plots each,
    (ii) the nine combinations of each pair of ingredients must be represented by one plot each.

If the set satisfies the second group of conditions it satisfies also the first. It is not, however, at first sight obvious that the second condition can be fulfilled at once for all three pairs of factors. The combinatorial relationship exhibited in the Latin square may here be applied most valuably.

Let us set out the nine combinations to be chosen in a diagrammatic square with three rows and three columns, and let us lay it down that treatments in the first row shall receive nitrogen at the first level, treatments in the second row at the second level, and treatments in the third row at the third level. Then the requirement that the three levels of nitrogen shall be equally represented in our selection is satisfied easily by having three plots in each row of our diagram. Similarly, we may lay it down that the columns of our square correspond to the levels of abundance of the second ingredient, potash, in the manurial mixture to be tested. It is then clear that we must have three plots in each column, and, if the interactions of nitrogen and potash are to be conserved, that there must be one plot at the intersection of each row with each column. With respect to the level at which phosphate is applied to any plot, we cannot now represent it by its position in our diagrammatic square, but shall simply use the numbers 1, 2, 3 inserted in any position in the diagram to represent the level of the phosphatic ingredient.

It now appears that a selection of nine treatments will satisfy the conditions laid down above, if it can be represented diagrammatically by a square containing nine numbers at the intersections of the three rows with the three columns, of which every row must contain 1, 2 and 3 once each, in order that the interaction of nitrogen and phosphorus should be conserved; and every column equally must contain a " 1," a " 2 " and a " 3," to make sure of conserving the interaction of potash and phosphorus. We have, in fact, merely to arrange the numbers 1, 2, 3 in a Latin square in order to obtain a single selection of the treatments, which might properly occupy a single block.

	k_1	k_2	k_3
n_1	1	2	3
n_2	2	3	1
n_3	3	1	2

There are only 12 solutions of the 3×3 Latin square. If we choose one of these to represent the contents of one block, we must next enquire whether any selection of treatments to occupy the other blocks in the same replications can be made to satisfy the conditions. We may convince ourselves on this point by considering the effect on our chosen selection of making a cyclic substitution of the levels of phosphate ; that is by substituting 2 for 1, 3 for 2, and 1 for 3 throughout the diagram. Repeating such a substitution three times will clearly bring us back to the original selection ; but the two new selections first produced will (i) both be represented by Latin squares, and (ii) will between them and the original from which they were derived contain all 27 treatments. This last essential fact becomes clear on perceiving that the number in any particular cell of the square must take the values 1, 2, 3 on successive applications of the substitution, whatever may be the initial value, while the aggregate of the 27 treatments used are represented simply by these three numbers, placed at all the nine points of the diagram.

The 26 independent comparisons among 27 treatments may be analysed according to the factors involved, as in the following table :—

TABLE 16

N	.	.	.	.	2
K	.	.	.	.	2
P	.	.	.	.	2
NK	.	.	.	.	4
PK	.	.	.	.	4
NP	.	.	.	.	4
NPK	.	.	.	.	8

Total . 26

If, therefore, we make up the contents of the block in accordance with the solution provided by the Latin square diagram, we shall have sacrificed a particular 2 out of the 8 degrees of freedom for triple interaction.

It is, of course, always easy to recognise the particular components of treatment in which blocks in the same replication differ, and to obtain the aggregate sum of squares for the six triple interactions which have not been confounded, by subtraction. This residue of unconfounded interactions may then be tested for significance like other treatment effects, and will usually be of service in confirming experimentally the supposition upon which the experimental design was based, namely, that the triple interactions as a whole had not been quantitatively important.

There is, however, a certain advantage in being able to recognise which particular contrasts these unconfounded interactions represent. For then we can, if we wish, subdivide them to examine the significance of more particular effects. In the case of the design under discussion, based on a 3 × 3 Latin square the combinatorial properties of such a square are such as to make this recognition easy. It has been mentioned above that there are only twelve 3 × 3 squares, and we have seen that each belongs to a set of 3 which can be generated from it by a cyclic substitution. There are,

therefore, only 4 such sets, and the 4 squares below are
representatives chosen one from each set.

	I.			II.			III.			IV.	
1	2	3	1	3	2	1	2	3	1	3	2
2	3	1	3	2	1	3	1	2	2	1	3
3	1	2	2	1	3	2	3	1	3	2	1

It may be observed that the second representative
is formed from the first by interchanging the numbers
2 and 3 ; the third is formed from the first by interchanging the second and third rows, and the fourth
is formed from the first by interchanging the second
and third columns. If we consider, now, examples
Nos. I. and II. it is to be observed that they agree in
the three plots having phosphate at level No. 1, but
differ in the other six. If, however, we applied the
cyclic substitution to the first example, it would, after
one operation, agree with the second example in the
three plots at phosphate level No. 3, and differ in the
other six ; while after a second operation it would
agree only in the three plots at phosphate level No. 2.
Consequently, the nine treatments in any selection of
set II. appear three each in the three selections of set I.,
these sets of treatments being those having the same
quantity of phosphate. The treatment comparisons
represented by the subdivision of the 27 treatments
as in set II. are therefore wholly independent of the
treatment comparisons of set I. Both represent 2
degrees of freedom out of the 8 available for triple
interaction, and these 2 pairs of degrees of freedom
have nothing in common. Consequently, when the
pair of degrees of freedom of set I. are confounded,
the pair represented by set II. are wholly conserved.

The same relationship subsists between set III. and
set I. if we consider the treatments represented in the

same row, *i.e.* those at an equal level of nitrogen, instead of those represented by the same number, at an equal level of phosphate. The examples shown above agree in the first row and differ in the two other rows. If the cyclic substitution be applied to the first example it will agree with the third successively in the second and third rows, while always differing in the remaining two. Consequently, the third set, like the second, represents a treatment contrast wholly independent of that represented by the first, and which is therefore entirely conserved if the latter is confounded. In like manner, the treatments in any selection of set IV. will be distributed by threes in the selections of set I., these threes lying in the same column, and having therefore equal quantities of potash. The 2 degrees of freedom of set IV. are also, therefore, wholly conserved. It should be noticed further that the three sets—II., III. and IV.—are not only independent of set I., but are also independent of each other. Thus in the examples shown, II. and III. agree in a single column, II. and IV. in a single row, and III. and IV. in a single number ; and, in view of what has been said above, these facts suffice to show that the pairs of degrees of freedom represented by these sets are wholly independent and have nothing in common. Since all are included in the 6 degrees of freedom conserved, they must therefore constitute the whole of the 6 degrees of freedom, and constitute parts of it which may be separated in the analysis and examined separately in the test of significance.

Supposing, then, that the experiment were carried out with 12 replications, or, in all, 324 plots, we might choose one of the 4 pairs of degrees of freedom into which the 8 triple interactions have been divided, and decide to sacrifice these particular components of the triple interactions, in order to increase the precision of the comparisons to be made in the 6 components of single factor effects, the 12 components of interactions between pairs of factors, and the 6 components of triple interactions which have not been confounded. The experiment then consists of 36 blocks of 9 plots each, so that 35 degrees of freedom are eliminated as representing block differences. The sets of treatments in different blocks within the same replication are assigned by using one of the cyclic sets of 3×3 Latin squares; remembering, of course, that topographically these treatments are not arranged in a Latin square, but are assigned at random to the 9 plots in the block. Each set of 9 treatments replicated 12 times will provide 88 degrees of freedom for error, or 264 in all, so that the complete analysis of the experiment may be shortly represented as below :—

TABLE 17

	Degrees of Freedom.
Blocks	35
Single factors	6
Interactions between pairs . .	12
Unconfounded triple interactions .	6
Error	264
Total . .	323

47. Partial Confounding

In the example we have just considered with 27 treatments it has been shown that we can gain the great advantage of smaller blocks, or increased homogeneity of material, for all the primary comparisons, and their interactions by pairs, at the expense of some sacrifice of information about the triple interactions, which are presumed to be comparatively unimportant. The advantage of such a procedure would be great in many practical cases, even if all knowledge of the interactions

of a higher order had to be forgone. Formally, however, the typical experiment discussed has shown that
the sacrifice required is that of one only of four portions
into which the triple interactions may be divided, and
that we may sacrifice whichever one we please of these
four portions. If, now, it is thought that knowledge
of these interactions, though admittedly comparatively
unimportant, is not wholly worthless, the fact that only
one-quarter has to be sacrificed will appear to be a real
advantage. This advantage is not, however, made
fully accessible by the experiment proposed; for the
6 degrees of freedom conserved, while they afford satisfactory guidance as to the significance or insignificance
of such triple interactions as may exist, represent
manurial contrasts of a somewhat complex kind, and
are not in fact the components we should choose for
separate examination if the triple interactions had been
conserved in their entirety.

When the quantity of an ingredient of a mixture
has been tested at three different levels the two independent comparisons which these provide may often
be usefully subdivided in a particular way. We may
regard the difference between the highest level and the
lowest as representing the principal effect of the
ingredient, that is, as giving us the average effect brought
about by a unit addition of this ingredient, averaged
over the range of dosage studied. In conjunction with
this principal degree of freedom we may introduce a
second, orthogonal to, or statistically independent of,
the first. This will be found by subtracting the sum of
the effects of the first and third level from twice the
effect of the second level of concentration. Thus if
(n_1), (n_2), (n_3) stand for different levels of the amount
of nitrogen in a manurial mixture, or for the measured
effects of such treatments, the two components of the

effect of nitrogen which may conveniently be separated
are defined by

$$N_1 = (n_3)-(n_1)$$

and

$$N_2 = 2(n_2)-(n_1)-(n_3).$$

These forms at least will be convenient when the con-
centrations tested differ by equal steps, or by steps
which, on any hypothesis under consideration, should
produce equal effects. They may be modified to other
orthogonal linear forms when the relationship between
the quantities used experimentally is of a more complicated character. Here we are concerned only to
illustrate the statement that when high order interactions
are regarded as having any experimental importance,
our interest will usually be centred on particular components into which such interactions may be analysed.
The statistical independence of the two forms proposed
above may be conveniently verified by multiplying
together the coefficients of (n_1) in the two expressions,
and adding the product so formed to the corresponding
products for the coefficients of (n_2) and (n_3). If these
products add up to zero the components designated are
statistically independent and represent mutually exclusive
degrees of freedom.

Considering the 4 degrees of freedom for the interaction of two ingredients, such as nitrogen and potash,
it is now readily seen that these can be denoted by the
four symbols, N_1K_1, N_2K_1, N_1K_2, and N_2K_2, any one
of which may be interpreted in terms of the treatments
concerned by algebraic expansion. Thus :—

$$N_1K_1 = (n_3-n_1)(k_3-k_1)$$
$$= (n_3k_3)-(n_1k_3)-(n_3k_1)+(n_1k_1),$$

and so with other expressions. It will be seen at once
that, if our interest in the interaction between nitro-

I

genous and potassic treatments arises principally from a suspicion that, with a larger supply of nitrogen, there may be a greater need for or opportunities for the utilisation of potash, then the particular component N_1K_1 will have an interest which the other components from which it has been separated do not share. Similarly, with triple interactions it might well be that the sole scientific interest of the eight independent comparisons which, in our experiment, these afford, lay in one particular component such as $N_1K_1P_1$.

The inconvenience of the confounding process used in the experiment consists, therefore, in the fact that if the triple interaction, or any component of it, is possibly of sufficient magnitude to be not wholly negligible, the components of triple interaction conserved by the experiment will not probably be themselves of any special interest, and, in the absence of the two components which have been confounded, will not afford the means of isolating the more interesting components for special study. It would seem, therefore, that it would have been preferable, if possible, to have spread such information, as the experiment is designed to give respecting the triple interactions, equally over the 8 degrees of freedom of which they are composed, unless the structure of the experiment is itself such as to isolate for conservation just those components which are of the greatest interest. The process of spreading the available information equally over the whole group of comparisons which are affected is known as partial confounding.

In our example there are 12 replications. If the number of replications, as in this case, is divisible by 4, then, instead of completely confounding a chosen pair of degrees of freedom out of the four pairs available, we might partially confound all four, by using each cyclic set three times instead of using the same set twelve times. The treatment comparison represented by any cyclic set will then have been conserved in 9 replications, while it has been sacrificed in 3. All these comparisons will therefore be capable of evaluation from the results of the experiment, though with only three-quarters of the precision with which interactions between pairs of factors and the effects of single factors have been evaluated. In such an arrangement the general advantage conferred by the principle of confounding may be most clearly seen, for the reduction in the size of the block from 27 plots to 9 will probably have increased the precision of the unconfounded comparisons in a higher ratio than that of $4 : 3$; and, as the triple interactions are only confounded in 1 replication out of 4, they also will be evaluated with increased, but more moderately increased, precision, in spite of the quarter of the information respecting them which has been sacrificed in order that the blocks might be reduced to 9 plots each.

The information concerning the triple interactions which has been supplied by the experiment, if partial confounding has been practised, will be in the form of contrasts between the three sets of 9 treatments, each

$$\begin{pmatrix} 1 & 2 & 3 \\ 2 & 3 & 1 \\ 3 & 1 & 2 \end{pmatrix}, \quad \begin{pmatrix} 2 & 3 & 1 \\ 3 & 1 & 2 \\ 1 & 2 & 3 \end{pmatrix}, \quad \begin{pmatrix} 3 & 1 & 2 \\ 1 & 2 & 3 \\ 2 & 3 & 1 \end{pmatrix},$$

specified by one of the four cyclic sets of Latin squares. These contrasts must be gathered separately from those parts of the experiment from which they are available, without using those parts in which they are confounded. By this means the comparison is kept unaffected by the larger elements of soil heterogeneity, which distinguish the different blocks. Thus the contrast between the three sets of treatments may be obtained by adding up the aggregate response to these sets of treatments, in the 9 replications in which these contrasts of manurial treatment are not those which characterise whole blocks. A different set of 9 replications will provide the material for evaluating the contrasts between the sets of treatments of the second group, namely,

$$\begin{pmatrix} 1 & 3 & 2 \\ 3 & 2 & 1 \\ 2 & 1 & 3 \end{pmatrix}, \quad \begin{pmatrix} 2 & 1 & 3 \\ 1 & 3 & 2 \\ 3 & 2 & 1 \end{pmatrix}, \quad \begin{pmatrix} 3 & 2 & 1 \\ 2 & 1 & 3 \\ 1 & 3 & 2 \end{pmatrix},$$

while different sets of nine replications will give the contrasts between the cyclic derivatives obtained from the squares

$$\begin{array}{ccc} 1 & 2 & 3 \\ 3 & 1 & 2 \\ 2 & 3 & 1 \end{array} \quad \text{and} \quad \begin{array}{ccc} 1 & 3 & 2 \\ 2 & 1 & 3 \\ 3 & 2 & 1 \end{array}$$

If, now, we are specially interested to evaluate a particular component of the triple interaction, such as that which has been denoted above by $N_1K_1P_1$, we must obtain this by a combination of the contrasts which the experiment provides directly. To do this may require some ingenuity. The solution in this case is found by using only those squares in which one diagonal, or the other, contains plots with the highest or lowest level of phosphate. Thus, if we compound with the proper positive and negative signs the yields given by the experiment for the 8 squares set out below, it appears that

$$\begin{pmatrix} 2 & 3 & 1 \\ 3 & 1 & 2 \\ 1 & 2 & 3 \end{pmatrix} - \begin{pmatrix} 1 & 2 & 3 \\ 2 & 3 & 1 \\ 3 & 1 & 2 \end{pmatrix} + \begin{pmatrix} 3 & 2 & 1 \\ 2 & 1 & 3 \\ 1 & 3 & 2 \end{pmatrix} - \begin{pmatrix} 2 & 1 & 3 \\ 1 & 3 & 2 \\ 3 & 2 & 1 \end{pmatrix}$$

$$+ \begin{pmatrix} 3 & 1 & 2 \\ 2 & 3 & 1 \\ 1 & 2 & 3 \end{pmatrix} - \begin{pmatrix} 1 & 2 & 3 \\ 3 & 1 & 2 \\ 2 & 3 & 1 \end{pmatrix} + \begin{pmatrix} 3 & 2 & 1 \\ 1 & 3 & 2 \\ 2 & 1 & 3 \end{pmatrix} - \begin{pmatrix} 1 & 3 & 2 \\ 2 & 1 & 3 \\ 3 & 2 & 1 \end{pmatrix}$$

is equal to $3\,N_1K_1P_1$.

With the aid of this example the reader will do well to consider how the data of the experiment should be combined to obtain other types of interaction, such as those denoted by $N_1K_1P_2$, $N_2K_2P_1$, and $N_2K_2P_2$, and to satisfy himself that these can each be derived by a similar choice of appropriate compounds from the data provided by the partially confounded experiment.

47·1. Practical Exercises

1. Show that, if each factor be tested at two levels, so many as fifteen factors can be tested in blocks of 16, without confounding any interaction of less than three factors.

2. In a linkage test with eight genetic factors, show that a selection of 8 out of the 128 possible types of multiple heterozygotes can be made so that each of the 28 pairs of factors is in " coupling " in 4, and in " repulsion " in 4.

3. Using a completely orthogonal 7×7 square, show that with eight replications a set of 49 varieties may be tested in blocks of 7, so that every possible pair of varieties occurs once only in the same block.

4. Show that the same may be done, in eight replications, with 57 varieties in blocks of 8, and that it cannot be done, in seven replications, with 43 varieties in blocks of 7.

5. Twenty-one experimental plants have each five leaves growing serially along the stem. Show how to allocate 21 treatments to the leaves, so that each pair of treatments occurs once on the same plant, and each treatment occurs once on a first leaf, and once on a leaf in the other ordinal positions. (Youden's Square.)

6. If 144 varieties be set out diagrammatically in a 12×12 square, and tested in blocks of 12, so that in one replication varieties in the same row fall in the

same block, and in a second replication the blocks contain varieties in the same column, show that the sampling variances of comparisons between pairs of varieties which (*a*) are, and (*b*) are not, tested in the same block, are in the ratio 13 : 14.

7. If 512 varieties be set out in an $8 \times 8 \times 8$ cube and tested in three replications in orthogonally chosen blocks of 8, compare the variances of the comparisons of any one variety with others which (*a*) occur in the same block as the first, (*b*) are connected with it at one remove through other varieties, and (*c*) are only connected at two removes (73 : 78 : 79).

REFERENCES AND OTHER READING

F. YATES (1933). The principles of orthogonality and confounding in replicated experiments. Journal of Agricultural Science, xxiii. 108-145.

F. YATES (1935). Complex experiments. Supplement to Journal of the Royal Statistical Society, vol. ii. 181-223.

F. YATES (1936). A new method of arranging variety trials involving a large number of varieties. Journal of Agricultural Science, xxvi. 424-455.

F. YATES (1936). Incomplete randomised blocks. Annals of Eugenics, vii. 121-140.

R. C. BOSE and K. KISHEN (1940). On the problem of confounding in the general symmetrical factorial design. Sankhya, v. 21-36.

R. C. BOSE and K. R. NAIR (1939). Partially balanced incomplete block designs. Sankhya, iv. 337-372.

R. A. FISHER and F. YATES (second edition 1942). Statistical Tables. Oliver and Boyd Ltd., Edinburgh.

R. A. FISHER (1942). New cyclic solutions to problems in incomplete blocks. Annals of Eugenics, xi. 290-299.

R. A. FISHER (1945). A system of confounding for factors with more than two alternatives, giving completely orthogonal cubes and higher powers. Annals of Eugenics, xii. 283-290.

VIII

SPECIAL CASES OF PARTIAL CONFOUNDING

48. TREATING of a subject such as experimental design in general, it is possible to give adequate space only to general principles leading to the more advantageous procedures which are available. These it is essential to grasp. Their applications to particular details that arise in practice are of endless variety and afford scope for a great deal of ingenuity. These require to be studied in detail by workers in different fields of experimentation in order to reap the full advantages which a clear grasp of general principles makes possible. It may be of use in this chapter if we consider some of the more special applications of the principle of partial confounding which were found to arise in their early application to field trials in agriculture.

49. Dummy Comparisons

It may happen that, in order that the different variants of each factor may occur with proportional frequency in combination with the variants of other factors, certain of the combinations used are actually indistinguishable. For example, in an experiment with four different nitrogenous manures we may also wish to vary the quantities used. We may wish to compare plots receiving no nitrogenous manure with others receiving a single or a double dressing. These single and double dressings will be applied to different plots, in each of the four nitrogenous materials to be tested, and the precision of the comparison between single and double applications will be enhanced by the fact that each is represented on four kinds of plots. In order that the comparison with the plots receiving no nitrogenous manure may be of equal precision, it is necessary that these shall be as numerous as those receiving single or double dressings, and therefore four times as numerous as any one kind of these. To compare the efficacy of the four kinds or qualities of nitrogen simultaneously with the three quantities (0, 1, 2) with which they can be combined, we might make blocks of 12 plots each, in which the plots receiving single or double dressings will be manured differently, while the 4 plots receiving none will all be manured alike. The comparisons among these within each block will be ascribable solely to experimental error, including in that term, as is usual, variations in the fertility of different plots in the same block. Thus, if there were 5 replications, the analysis of the 59 independent comparisons among the 60 plots would not be

TABLE 18

	Degrees of Freedom.
Blocks	4
Treatments	11
Error	44
Total . .	59

but

TABLE 19

		Degrees of Freedom.
Blocks		4
Treatments		8
Error { between blocks		32
{ within blocks		15
Total . .		59

Here we have divided the 47 degrees of freedom available for the estimation of error into two parts, to show that 15 degrees of freedom come from a comparison of identical plots in the same block, 3 from each of the five blocks, while 32 come from the comparison of the differences among the 9 different treatments in the five blocks in which they are tried.

As between the two factors of quantity of nitrogen N, and quality Q, the 8 degrees of freedom between the 9 treatments will be allotted as follows. There will be 2 for the comparison of the three levels of the nitrogen, and 3 for the four qualitatively different mixtures in which it is applied, leaving 3 more for interactions between N and Q. In other words we have, as we would have if the four manures were applied only in single and double doses, 3 degrees for quality and 3 for interaction. The addition of the plots without the nitrogenous manure has left these two classes unaffected, but has added 1 to the degrees of freedom for quantity of nitrogen.

50. Interaction of Quantity and Quality

In this connection a modification is to be indicated in the manner in which the effects of quality and inter-action are to be reckoned. If we were to consider N and Q as two independent factors, the 3 degrees of freedom for interaction would be obtained simply by com-parison of the four quantities by which the double appli-cations of each manure exceed the effects of single applications of the same materials. Equally, the simple qualitative effects would be represented by the contrast between the four totals of single and double dressings of these four materials. Such a subdivision is seen to be not wholly satisfactory, when we consider that the quantitative contrasts are differences caused by quanti-tative variations in the very substances which the qualitative comparisons are intended to compare. Thus, if a quantity of nitrogen applied as cyanamide differs in its effect on the crop from an equal quantity of nitrogen applied as urea, it is to be anticipated that with larger quantities of the manurial applications the difference would be enhanced.   In fact, the hypothesis that the differences are proportional to the quantities of nitrogen applied is in many ways a simpler one, in the sense of being more natural and acceptable, than that the difference should be the same irrespective of the quantities of material added to the soil.

If we take this view, results in which the double dressings of two ingredients differ by twice as much as the single dressings, but in the same direction, would be regarded as exhibiting pure effects of quality Q, without interaction NQ.   The interactions must, therefore, be identified with the three independent comparisons among the four quantities which would be obtained by subtracting the yield of the double dressing from twice the yield of the corresponding single dressing. For these four quantities would all be equal if interaction, in the sense in which we are now using this term, were completely absent.   Equally, the primary effects of quality will now be reckoned by comparing the four sums found by adding twice the yield of the double application to the yield from the single application of the same manure ; as in calculating the "regression" of the manurial response upon the manurial difference to which it is for the present purpose to be considered as proportional.   The statistical principles and methods in the treatment of regression are developed in *Statistical Methods for Research Workers*.

That these two methods give different subdivisions of the same total follows from the algebraic identity

$$\tfrac{1}{2}(x+y)^2+\tfrac{1}{2}(x-y)^2 = \tfrac{1}{5}(2x+y)^2+\tfrac{1}{5}(x-2y)^2$$

If x, y stand for the yields of the double and single dressings of any manurial material, the two terms on the left represent the squares assigned to Q and NQ, using the convention that " interaction " means variation in the values $x-y$, while the two terms on the right represent the squares assigned to Q and NQ on the convention that " interaction " means variation among the values $x-2y$. The same method of subdivision with appropriate coefficients is evidently applicable whatever may be the ratio between the quantities used. Note that the divisor of each square is the sum of the squares of the coefficients, while the sum of the products of the coefficients in any two squares of the same set is zero.

51. Resolution of Three Comparisons among Four Materials

The 3 degrees of freedom in Q or in NQ are the three independent comparisons among four different materials, such as sulphate of ammonia (s), chloride of ammonia (m), cyanamide (c), and urea (u). These may be systematically subdivided, if it is thought convenient to do so, as the three possible comparisons between opposing pairs of materials. There are in fact just three ways of dividing four objects into two sets of two each ; these are :—

$$s+m-c-u$$
$$s-m+c-u$$
$$s-m-c+u,$$

and these are all mutually independent, as may be verified by observing that the sum of the products of the coefficients ($+1$, or -1) of the symbols in any two of these three expressions is zero.

Regarded combinatorially, this is equivalent to the statement that a 2×2 Latin square is possible, namely,

$$A \quad B$$
$$B \quad A,$$

for in such a square the four objects are divided into pairs in three ways, as rows, as columns, and as letters, and the specification of a Latin square requires that these shall all be mutually independent.

52. An Early Example

An experiment with sulphate of ammonia, chloride of ammonia, cyanamide and urea, in quantities 0, 1, 2, with and without superphosphate, was carried out in barley at Rothamsted in 1927. Two replications, or 48 plots, were used. These were divided into four blocks of 12 plots each. In two blocks phosphate (p) was applied with chloride of ammonia and with urea, in both single and double dressings, while in the other two blocks it was applied with sulphate of ammonia and with cyanamide. Each block contained two plots without nitrogenous or phosphatic dressings, and two plots with phosphatic only. The plots were assigned to treatments at random within the blocks.

Among the 18 different treatments there will be 17 independent comparisons. One of these, however, namely,

$$(p-1)(s_1+s_2-m_1-m_2+c_1+c_2-u_1-u_2)$$

has been confounded with blocks. There are 16 degrees of freedom for treatments in the analysis, and 3 for blocks, leaving 28 for error. It would, however, be a mistake to assume from this that these 28 are all pure error, for it will appear that owing to the occurrence of dummy treatments, or more properly of plots treated alike in different blocks of the same replication, the degree of freedom destined to be sacrificed has in fact only been partially confounded.

It is instructive in such cases to consider exactly what comparisons will consist solely of error, unaffected by any treatment differences. Within each block there are two unmanured plots the difference between which is pure error, and two phosphatic plots of which the

	A				B		
$(u_2 p)$ 480	$(m_2 p)$ 542	(c_2) 373	(1) 186	(1) 268	(p) 297	$(s_2 p)$ 536	$(s_1 p)$ 471
$(m_1 p)$ 431	(c_1) 365	(s_2) 293	(s_1) 281	(u_1) 343	$(c_2 p)$ 443	(u_2) 498	(m_2) 522
(p) 284	(p) 313	$(u_1 p)$ 336	(1) 260	(m_1) 366	$(c_1 p)$ 412	(p) 250	(1) 239
(u_2) 475	(1) 275	(1) 242	$(c_2 p)$ 395	(p) 244	(c_2) 396	(s_2) 400	(p) 228
(p) 344	(p) 277	$(s_1 p)$ 359	(m_1) 368	(s_1) 413	$(u_2 p)$ 512	(1) 259	$(m_1 p)$ 453
(u_1) 401	$(c_1 p)$ 429	$(s_2 p)$ 464	(m_2) 542	$(m_2 p)$ 504	(c_1) 409	$(u_1 p)$ 389	(1) 267
	C				D		

FIG. 2.—Arrangement of treatments and yields of grain in experiment on quantity and quality of nitrogenous fertilisers in barley 1927.

same is true. Here, therefore, we have 8 degrees of freedom contributing only to our estimate of error. To make sure that these are not counted a second time, it is sufficient that all further comparisons to be made, if they involve these plots, shall involve only the pairs of plots treated alike taken together. Next, observe that there are two pairs of blocks with the same treatments, 10 in each. The 10 differences between the performances of these in the two blocks of a pair will be distributed about a mean representing the difference in fertility between the two blocks ; but the 9 degrees of freedom of their variation about this mean will be pure error. There are thus 9 degrees of freedom from each pair of blocks, or 18 together, which, with the 8 from within blocks, make 26 in all. In subsequent comparisons we must, however, treat the two blocks of each pair together. Finally, the two pairs of blocks have two treatments in common, those unmanured and those having phosphate only. The differences between these two treatments in the two pairs of blocks will not be necessarily the same, and the discrepancy between them will be pure error ; this last degree of freedom makes up the total to 27.

The yields of grain from each plot in units of 2 oz. are shown in Fig. 2 ; the contributions to the sum of squares ascribable to these 27 degrees of freedom of pure error are shown in Table 20.

Squares involving two plots only are divided by 2, others such as the first two entries in the second and third columns depend on 4 plots, and are divided by 4, and the squares of differences between pairs of blocks by 24. Finally, the discrepancy of 47 units between $(p)-(1)$ from the two pairs of blocks depends on 16 plots, and has its square divided by 16. The several ingredients are thus brought to a comparable basis.

It was mentioned above that the single manurial contrast

$$(p-1)(s_1+s_2-m_1-m_2+c_1+c_2-u_1-u_2)$$

in which the blocks differ, had not been totally confounded, meaning by this that it could be indirectly estimated by comparisons within blocks. The comparison within blocks, independent of all those used in the estimation of error, which depends only on this one manurial contrast, arises from the fact that though the

TABLE 20

Analysis of Components of Error

Squares of Differences between like Plots in the same Block.	Squares of Differences between like Treatments in like Blocks.			
(p) . . 841	(p) . . 7812·5		(1) . . 50	
(1) . . 5476	(1) . . 3200		(p) . . 2738	
(p) . . 2209	$(u_1 p)$ . . 2809		(u_1) . . 3364	
(1) . . 841	(c_1) . . 1936		$(c_1 p)$ . . 289	
(p) . . 4489	(s_1) . . 17424		$(s_1 p)$ . . 12544	
(1) . . 1089	$(m_1 p)$ . . 484		(m_1) . . 4	
(p) . . 256	$(u_2 p)$ . . 1024		(u_2) . . 529	
(1) . . 64	(c_2) . . 529		$(c_2 p)$ . . 2304	
———	(s_2) . . 11449		$(s_2 p)$ . . 5184	
15265	$(m_2 p)$ . . 1444		(m_2) . . 400	
	Total . −9075		Total . −456·3	
	39036·5		26949·6	

Differences $(p)-(1)$ in Pairs of Blocks.		Summary of Contributions to Pure Error.	
		Degrees of Freedom.	Sum of Squares.
A 151		8	7632·5
D . . . . −54		9	19518·25
———		9	13474·8$\frac{1}{3}$
A+D 97		1 $47^2 \div 16$	138·0625
B 40		—	———
C 104		27	40763·6458$\frac{1}{3}$
B+C 144			
A+D 97			
B+C−A−D . 47			

treatments concerned are not to be found in the same block, yet the different blocks in which they appear also contain some plots treated alike, with which each group can be compared.   In each block, in fact, we may compare the plots having single and double dressings of nitrogen with twice the sum of the plots having none. Thus two blocks give

$$(ps_1)+(ps_2)+(m_1)+(m_2)+(pc_1)+(pc_2)$$
$$+(u_1)+(u_2)-2(p)-2(p)-2(1)-2(1) = 1483, 1157;$$
$$\text{B} \qquad \text{C}$$

while the other two give

$$(s_1)+(s_2)+(pm_1)+(pm_2)+(c_1)+(c_2)+(pu_1)$$
$$+(pu_2)-2(p)-2(p)-2(1)-2(1) = 1015, 1480;$$
$$\text{A} \qquad \text{D}$$

whence we obtain by subtraction

$$(p-1)(s_1+s_2-m_1-m_2+c_1+c_2-u_1-u_2) = 145.$$

The value for each block is a combination of 8 plots with coefficient $+1$, and 4 plots with coefficient -2, so the sum of the squares is 24, or for the four blocks, 96. The contribution to the sum of squares of this partially confounded manurial comparison is therefore $145^2 \div 96$, or $219 \cdot 0104$.   To the divisor, 96, the plots having the treatments to be compared contribute only 32, so that the comparison is made with only one-third of the precision of the 16 unconfounded comparisons.

The other elements in the analysis may now be evaluated.   The 3 degrees of freedom between blocks are easily found to account for a contribution of $12,215 \cdot 75$ to the sum of squares.   The total effect of treatments could now be obtained by subtraction of the three items already evaluated from the total; the interest of the experiment, however, lies in evaluating the separate factors of the treatment differences.   The total yields, contributed by 8 plots each, in the six classes of treatment formed by combining two levels of phosphate with three of nitrogen, are shown in Table 21.

TABLE 21

	No Nitrogen.	Single Nitrogen.	Double Nitrogen.	Total.
With phosphate . . .	2237	3280	3876	9,393
Without phosphate . .	1996	2946	3499	8,441
Sum	4233	6226	7375	17,834
Difference	241	334	377	952

Plots receiving phosphate have exceeded those not receiving phosphate in all by 952 units, so that the 1 degree of freedom, P, contributes $952^2 \div 48$, or $18,881 \cdot \dot{3}$.

We may next take the 2 degrees of freedom for quantity of nitrogen N, and 2 more for interaction with phosphate NP.

The 2 degrees of freedom for N are evidently found by comparing the sums 4233, 6226, 7375 ; clearly the principal effect, the contrast between double nitrogen and none, is the important part ; the difference 3142 from 32 plots contributes the large item $3142^2 \div 32$, or $308,505 \cdot 125$ for N_1. The remaining degree of freedom, corresponding to diminishing return for the second dose of nitrogen, is found by subtracting the first and last totals from twice the total for single nitrogen, squaring, and dividing by 96. This gives $844^2 \div 96$, or $7420 \cdot 1\dot{6}$ for N_2, a much smaller, but still a significant, value. We may treat the differences in the same way. For $N_1 P$ we have $136^2 \div 32$, or 578, and for $N_2 P$ $50^2 \div 96$, or $26 \cdot 041\dot{6}$, both quite insignificant contributions, though in both cases of the expected sign. The items evaluated so far are :—

K

TABLE 22

	Degrees of Freedom.	Sum of Squares.
N_1	I	308505·125
N_2	I	7420·167
P	I	18881·333
NP	2	604·042

We may now consider the qualitative differences Q, and their interaction with quantity NQ. The totals from 4 plots each for the single and double application of the four nitrogenous nutrients are shown in Table 23.

TABLE 23

Quantity.	Material.				Differences between Pairs.		
	s.	m.	c.	u.	$s+m$ $-(c+u)$	$m+u$ $-(s+c)$	$m+c$ $-(s+u)$
(1)	1524	1618	1615	1469	...	...	...
(2)	1693	2110	1607	1965	...	...	...
2(2)+(1)	4910	5838	4829	5399	520	1498	358
2(1)−(2)	1355	1126	1623	973	−115	−879	421

The 3 degrees of freedom for Q and for NQ can now be found either by taking the sums of the squares of the deviations from their means, of the last two lines and dividing by 20, or by splitting the columns in the three possible ways into two opposed pairs, and dividing by 80. The latter process gives :—

TABLE 24

	Squares of Differences. Q	Squares of Differences. NQ
$s+m-c-u$ . .	270400	13225
$m+u-s-c$ . .	2244004	772641
$m+c-s-u$ . .	128164	177241
	2642568	963107

Q . . 33032·1   NQ . . 12038·8375

being each for 3 degrees of freedom. The separate evaluation of these three comparisons as above brings to light the somewhat suspicious circumstance that the largest contribution in each class is from the particular contrast between nitrogenous materials which has been used (in its interaction with phosphate) for confounding. If it is a coincidence that the two pairs of nutrients most contrasted in their effects on yield, and in their interaction with quantity of nitrogen have been chosen for the purpose, then the choice has been an unfortunate one. If not, then we may suspect that the conditions in the different blocks of land used have, in some obscure way, influenced the apparent reaction to these nutrients.

Had we adopted the subdivision between Q and NQ by means of the sums $(2)+(1)$ and differences $(2)-(1)$, we should have $21,739 \cdot 094$ for Q and $23,331 \cdot 844$ for NQ, making the same total, but giving a larger contribution for interaction than for the prime factors of quality. The subdivision employed above is therefore preferable, as based on a view of qualitative differences more in keeping with the facts.

The remaining interactions of phosphate with the quality of the nitrogenous application QP, and of phosphate with quality and quantity of nitrogen NQP, may be evaluated in a manner similar to Q and NQ, using the differences in place of the sums of the plots which have and have not received phosphate. In this group, however, we must remember that a particular component involving the contrast

$$(s-m+c-u)$$

has been confounded with blocks. The differences in yield between plots receiving phosphate and those receiving none are shown in the following table :—

TABLE 25

Quantity.	Material.				Differences between Pairs.		
	s.	m.	c.	u.	$m+s$ $-c-u$	$m+u$ $-s-c$	$s+u$ $-c-m$
(1)	136	150	67	−19	...	...	...
(2)	307	−18	69	19	...	...	...
2 (2)+(1)	750	114	205	19	640	(822)	450
2 (1)−(2)	−35	318	65	−57	275	(−231)	−475

The two unconfounded comparisons in the group QP make therefore a contribution evaluated by summing the squares of 640 and 450 and dividing by 80. This gives 7651·25 for these 2 degrees of freedom. The two corresponding components of NQP is the sum of the squares of 275 and 475 divided by 80, or 3765·625. The manurial comparison which has been confounded, namely,

$$(p-1)(s_1+s_2-m_1-m_2+c_1+c_2-u_1-u_2)$$

is not precisely a component either of QP or of NQP, as we have defined these groups. It would be a component of QP on the alternative definition discussed above, and the remaining unconfounded portion is the component of NQP of that definition, namely,

$$(p-1)(s_2-s_1-m_2+m_1+c_2-c_1-u_2+u_1).$$

This gives $303^2 \div 32$, or 2869·031.

The complete analysis of the variations observed among the yields of the 48 plots may therefore be set out as in the Table 26.

The total sum of squares for the 47 degrees of freedom, which have above been evaluated individually, must check with the sum of the squares of the deviations of the yields from the 48 plots from their mean without regard to the manurial treatments they have received,

or to their topographical arrangement. This affords a
check both on the arithmetic and on the logic of our
procedure, at least so far as to show that it has consisted
in a subdivision or partition of the different components
of variation actually present.

TABLE 26

	Degrees of Freedom.	Sum of Squares.	Mean Square.	$\frac{1}{2}$ Log$_e$
Blocks	3	12215·750	...	...
N$_1$	1	308505·125	308505·125	2·8659
P	1	18881·333	18881·333	1·4691
Q	3	33032·100	11010·700	1·1995
N$_2$	1	7420·167	7420·167	1·0021
NQ	3	12038·838	4012·946	0·6948
QP	2	7651·250	3825·625	0·6709
NP	2	604·042	302·021	...
NQP	2	3765·625	1881·812	...
NQP ⎱ unconfounded .	1	2869·031	2869·031	...
QP ⎰ confounded .	1	219·010	219·010	...
Error	27	40763·646	1509·765	0·2060
	47	447965·917		

Next, it may be noticed that the confounding
employed has involved a component of treatment
recognisable as an interaction of P with one of the
quality comparisons Q, but not identifiable with either
of the particular aspects which we have thought it
proper to recognise respectively as QP and NQP. It
thus resembles the components confounded in the experiment with 27 treatments, discussed in Chapter VII.,
and, as in that case, would be a source of inconvenience
if the unconfounded component observed were one of
any importance. The table shows, however, that in
the present case the component in question is of no
practical interest.

53. Interpretation of Results

The treatment comparisons in the table have been arranged to show first those which have had a significant influence on the yield of grain, next those in which there may perhaps be an indication of real influence, but of a magnitude which could only be demonstrated by more precise experimentation, and finally those which in the present experiment appear to have exerted no appreciable effect. By far the largest contribution is made by what we have called the principal effect of nitrogen, this 1 degree of freedom containing indeed more than two-thirds of the total. The mean square is over 200 times the mean square for error, or, since $\sqrt{200}$ exceeds 14, we may see at once that the general effect of nitrogen in this experiment is over 14 times its standard error, and is therefore determined with comparatively high precision. The single degree of freedom for phosphate has a mean square over twelve times the average, showing that this effect also is certainly significant, though the quantitative value of this ingredient has been evaluated only roughly.

The statistical significance of each contribution to the total is most easily determined from the last column, which shows the half values of the natural logarithms of the mean squares. The table of z (*Statistical Methods*, Table VI.) shows that, with 27 degrees of freedom for error, the amount by which this entry may exceed that for error, at a 5 per cent. level of significance, is

·7187 for 1 degree of freedom
·6051 ,, 2 degrees ,,
and ·5427 ,, 3 ,, ,,

The corresponding values for significance at the 1 per cent. level are 1·0191, 0·8513 and 0·7631. The value for Q is therefore significant on the higher standard

(1 per cent.) and that for N_2 at the lower standard (5 per cent.). We may therefore take the values of Table 23 to indicate that chloride of ammonia was really more successful than sulphate of ammonia or cyanamide in stimulating grain production, with urea in an intermediate position, and that the second nitrogenous application was in general less fruitful than the first.

The mean squares for NQ and for QP, though considerably larger than that for error, do not reach the 5 per cent. level of significance. It therefore appears that the suggestion of the figures of Table 23 that chloride of ammonia and urea are not only more successful than sulphate of ammonia and cyanamide, but are disproportionately so in the double application, though supported by the data, is not demonstrated ; and that the suggestion of Table 25 that when sulphate of ammonia is used superphosphate is more effective than with the other nitrogenous fertilisers, must also be regarded as doubtful. The remaining 6 degrees of freedom, ascribable to manurial treatment, are clearly insignificant to such an extent that it would have made no appreciable difference if their effects had been included with those of pure error. This circumstance shows that the principle used in the choice of a component for confounding was in fact justified by the result. Their separate evaluation serves to show how this can be done whenever necessary, and supplies the safeguard that our positive conclusions are based on an estimate of error uncontaminated by possible interactions among the treatments.

This example illustrates the fact that when quantitative and qualitative factors are combined in the same experiment, the special meaning of their interactions may well be taken into account in experimental design.

Especially, when the quantities involved include zero, some of the treatment comparisons vanish, leading, on the one hand, to an increase of the comparisons available for error, and sometimes also to the partial recovery of comparisons which would otherwise have been totally confounded. The reader should consider the effects of one simple modification of the design used, by supposing that the component

$$(p-1)(s_1+s_2-m_1-m_2+c_1+c_2-u_1-u_2)$$

were confounded with one pair of blocks, and the component

$$(p-1)(s_1-s_2-m_1+m_2+c_1-c_2-u_1+u_2)$$

with the other.

54. An Experiment with 81 Plots

In considering the experiment with 27 treatments in Chapter VII., it was shown that these could be arranged in blocks of 9 at the expense of confounding 2 of the degrees of freedom representing triple interactions. It was also shown that when replication can be carried out in multiples of 4, the confounding could be spread equally over the whole of these 8 degrees of freedom, so that all triple interactions could be recovered with some relative loss of precision, though possibly an absolute increase. When quantitative and qualitative factors are combined in the same experiment there is little point in restricting the effects of confounding to the triple interactions as defined for the purpose of that example. Moreover, it is often necessary to see what can be done in experiments of less than 108 plots. The following design, which was carried out in potatoes at Rothamsted in 1931, shows a method of utilising 81 plots so as to gain the principal advantages which the experiment was intended to secure.

The factors to be tested were three levels in the ratio 0, 1, 2 of nitrogenous manure in combination with three similar levels of potassic manures. The potassium was to be supplied in three qualitatively different materials, namely, potassium sulphate (*s*), potassium chloride (*m*), and a material known as potash manure salts (*p*), consisting of potassium chloride with a large admixture of common salt. The plots were divided in 9 blocks of 9 plots each, each block containing one plot with every possible combination of the three levels of nitrogen with the three levels of potash. The 3 plots without potash therefore received respectively 0, 1 and 2 doses of nitrogen. The same was true of the 3 plots receiving a single potassic dressing, and of the 3 plots receiving double potassic dressings ; but in the case of these we have to choose in which form the potassium shall be supplied. In fact, at each level of potash one plot received sulphate, one chloride, and the third potash manure salts. The only ways in which the blocks can differ consist in the manner in which the three kinds of potash in each level are assigned to plots receiving 0, 1 or 2 quantities of nitrogen.

Considering only plots receiving single potassic dressings, we may designate those which receive sulphate of potash with 0, 1 and 2 quantities of nitrogen by s_0, s_1 and s_2. Then the set of plots at this level within any block will have some such formula as $s_0 m_1 p_2$, or, if we make the convention that the suffices are to be taken in their natural order, simply by $s\,m\,p$. If, now, corresponding to the block or blocks represented by the formula $s\,m\,p$, there are equal numbers of blocks represented by the formulæ $m\,p\,s$ and $p\,s\,m$, it is clear that the 9 kinds of plots which receive single potassic dressings will occur in the experiment in equal numbers ;

and, in fact, that we may assign 3 of our blocks to each of these formulæ. We might equally have used the formulæ *s p m, p m s* and *m s p*, but our choice is limited to these two cyclic sets. The same is true of the specification of the blocks in respect of the plots within them which receive a double dressing of potash. The particular design we shall consider is that formed by choosing one of these cyclic sets for single potash, making a similar choice for the double potash, and finally deciding that each of the 3 blocks which have the same formula at one level of potash shall have three different formulæ at the other, so that the 9 blocks are all assigned to different sets of treatments. They are all alike, in sets of three, at one level of potash, and in different sets of three at the other level, like the rows and columns of a 3 × 3 square.

As in the previous example, let us now consider which comparisons are available for estimation of error, and which remain for estimations of the effects of treatments. Since the three treatments without potash are the same in every block, the comparisons among this group will at once yield 16 degrees of freedom. At the level of single potash the three treatments are the same in sets of three blocks each, so that each set yields 4 degrees of freedom for error, or 12 in all. A second group of 12 is provided by the level of double potash, bringing the total for comparisons made between plots at the same level of potash up to 40. We must now confine ourselves to comparisons in which plots with the same potassic dressing in the same block are treated together. Comparing the plots receiving single potash with those receiving none in the same block, we see that this comparison is the same in three sets of three blocks each, giving 6 degrees of freedom, while six more are obtained by comparing the double potash plots with those without potash in the same block.* There are thus 52 degrees of freedom ascribable solely to experimental error. Together with 8 for comparisons between whole blocks, and 20 for comparisons among the 21 different treatments, we have enumerated the whole of the 80 degrees of freedom in the experiment. There could be no more contributions to pure error, unless some one or more of the treatment comparisons had been totally confounded with block differences.

We may now consider the manurial comparisons. There are seven combinations of quantity and quality of potash, the six comparisons among which may be resolved into 2 for quantity K, 2 for quality Q, and the remaining 2 for interaction of quantity and quality KQ. The distinction between Q and KQ will be made by the same convention as in the last example. Variation of the quantity of nitrogen increases the number of manurial combinations to 21 and therefore introduces 14 new comparisons. Of these, 2 represent the effects of quantity of nitrogen only N, 4 the interactions of quantitative variations of nitrogen and potash NK, 4 the interactions of quantity of nitrogen with quality of potash NQ, and 4 more the triple interaction NKQ. All these groups of comparisons, except those denoted NQ and NKQ, are obviously free from confounding, for they can be made up directly by comparisons within blocks. It is only the last 8 degrees of freedom which require special consideration. As often happens, and as the previous examples have already illustrated, we shall best see what has happened

* The last two sets of six components each are not, however, independent, since the plots without potash are used in both. The sum of squares for all twelve is most simply obtained by deducting from the 26 degrees of freedom among the totals from each block for the 0, 1, and 2 levels of potash, the 2 degrees of freedom for K, the 8 for blocks and the 4 partially confounded effects of treatment which will be identified later.

to this group of comparisons by resolving them into components in a way specially appropriate to the structure of the experiment.

Since qualitative differences exist only in plots receiving either single or double potassic dressings, the eight comparisons, with which we are concerned, are equivalent to the four representing interactions of nitrogen with quality of potash on the plots receiving single potassic dressings, together with the similar four on the plots receiving double potassic dressings. Let us consider these two parts separately. Just as the three independent comparisons among the four nitrogenous materials of the last example were subdivided in the same manner as the contrasts between rows, columns and letters in a 2 × 2 Latin square, so we shall now use the analogous property which a 3 × 3 square possesses. Let the rows of such a square correspond to the quantities 0, 1 and 2 of nitrogen and the columns to the three sorts, s, m and p of potash. Then three of our blocks have, in respect to the single potash dressings, the formula $s\,p\,m$. These we may call blocks of type A and insert the letter A in the three corresponding cells of the square. There will also be blocks with the formula $p\,m\,s$, which we may call type B, and with the formula $m\,s\,p$ which we may call type C. If these letters be inserted we shall have a 3 × 3 Latin square as shown below :—

		Kind of Potash.		
Quantity of nitrogen	. 0	Aα	Cβ	Bγ
„ „	. 1	Cγ	Bα	Aβ
„ „	. 2	Bβ	Aγ	Cα

To the Latin letters in the square, Greek letters have been added, in such a way that each appears once in each column, once in each row and once with each Latin letter. The whole thus constitutes what is known

as a Græco-Latin square.   The fact that a Græco-
Latin square is possible shows that the eight independent
comparisons among nine objects can be resolved into
four independent sets of 2 degrees of freedom each,
each pair being the comparison between three sets of
three chosen objects each.   These are the two comparisons among rows, two among columns, two among
Latin letters, and two among Greek letters.   It will be
observed that the comparisons among Latin letters have
been chosen to correspond with the differences among
the sets of blocks ; consequently, the comparisons
among the Greek letters are independent of these block
differences, and, like the comparisons between rows N
and columns Q, may be made by comparing yields
within the same block.   By adding up the yields of all
plots having treatments of the combinations indicated
by the letters α, β and γ, we may evaluate two treatment
comparisons which have not been confounded.   Two
more are likewise obtained from the plots with double
potassic dressings.   In this way four of the eight comparisons represented by NQ and NKQ are isolated.
The 4 remaining degrees have, however, been partially
confounded.

The confounding of these four remaining comparisons
with block differences is incomplete, owing to the fact
that the blocks, which differ in respect of them, agree
in containing other plots treated alike, with which they
may be compared.   Thus, in the three blocks of type A,
the plots with single dressings of potash having the
chosen constitutions s_0, p_1 and m_2 are situated in the
same blocks with an aggregate of plots receiving no
potash, and with an aggregate receiving double potash,
both of which are the same as the aggregates which
occur in the three blocks of type B, and in the three
blocks of type C.   We may therefore compare the total

yield from the treatments s_0, p_1 and m_2 with the totals from the other sets of treatments p_0, m_1 and s_2, and

TABLE 27

Arrangement and Yields of a Complex Experiment
$(s\,p\,m)_1$ $(s\,m\,p)_2$

n_1m_2	n_0s_2	n_0s_1	n_1	n_2p_1	n_1s_2	n_2s_1	n_1p_2	n_2
751	733	686	851	890	874	1026	947	990
844	829	825	800	733	813	1050	871	1006
n_0	n_2	n_1p_1	n_0	n_2m_2	n_0p_2	n_2s_2	n_0m_2	n_0p_1
796	910	909	855	1026	865	1118	853	795
705	866	778	779	815	816	997	953	843
n_1	n_2m_1	n_2p_2	n_2	n_0m_1	n_1s_1	n_0	n_1	n_1m_1
895	1034	1052	913	756	892	1024	972	975
965	1046	830	752	830	930	979	1000	884
n_0	n_0m_1	n_0m_2	n_0s_2	n_2s_1	n_1m_1	n_1s_2	n_0	n_2m_2
1100	1014	975	956	1037	1035	1284	1012	1001
996	968	902	898	975	1027	1176	966	977
n_1s_1	n_1p_2	n_2s_2	n_0	n_0p_1	n_1m_2	n_2	n_0s_1	n_1
1029	1121	1252	1058	1038	1098	1316	1136	1087
1022	961	1127	1006	904	1206	1275	1049	1001
n_1	n_2p_1	n_2	n_2	n_2p_2	n_1	n_0p_2	n_2m_1	n_1p_1
959	1178	1317	1270	1234	1195	1307	1224	1069
930	1102	1145	1118	1134	1132	1348	1275	1128
n_2	n_2m_2	n_0p_1	n_1	n_1p_1	n_2s_2	n_2p_2	n_1m_2	n_0
1131	1140	1055	1151	1147	1156	1401	1214	1005
1034	1156	1026	1044	1056	1228	1391	1321	1011
n_1m_1	n_1s_2	n_1	n_2m_1	n_1p_2	n_2	n_0s_2	n_2	n_0m_1
980	1243	1224	1192	1225	1305	1310	1421	1190
1027	1065	1064	1199	1120	1276	1339	1417	1208
n_0	n_0p_2	n_2s_1	n_0m_2	n_0s_1	n_0	n_1s_1	n_1	n_2p_1
1020	653	935	629	947	1020	1361	1167	1222
605	999	1142	1056	1049	1102	1201	1215	1108

m_0, s_1 and p_2, by subtracting in each block the sum of the yields from plots without potash, and with double potash, from twice the yield of the plots with single potash, and adding together the results from blocks in which the plots with single potash have been treated alike. The manurial comparisons so made clearly represent two of those which have been confounded with blocks, but which can be made, in the manner explained above, by means of comparisons wholly within blocks, with a satisfactory precision. The sum of the squares of the coefficients of the expression

$$2k_1 - k_0 - k_2$$

is 6, and to this total the coefficient of k_1 contributes 4. Consequently, the comparison so made among the different sets of plots receiving single potash has two-thirds of the precision of the other comparisons of the experiment, and so, perhaps, a higher precision than they would have had, even if unconfounded, in an experiment with 27 plots to each block.

The student may familiarise himself with the process of analysis described above by applying it to the yields of tubers in quarter-lbs. shown in Table 27 of the arrangement of the treatments in different plots.

The upper and lower figures represent yields with and without phosphate, which was applied as an additional manure to half, chosen at random, of each plot. The sums of these yields may therefore be analysed as explained above, but their differences, representing the effects of the phosphatic manure, and its interactions, are already freed from all block effects, and will have their own standard error estimated directly from the discrepancies between these differences in plots treated alike.

REFERENCES AND OTHER READING

T. Eden and R. A. Fisher (1929). Experiments on the response of the potato to potash and nitrogen. Journal of Agricultural Science, xix. 201-213.

R. A. Fisher and J. Wishart (1930). The arrangement of field experiments and the statistical reduction of the results. Imperial Bureau of Soil Science, Technical Communication, No. 10.

F. Yates (1937) The design and analysis of factorial experiments. Imperial Bureau of Soil Science.

IX

THE INCREASE OF PRECISION BY CON-COMITANT MEASUREMENTS. STATISTICAL CONTROL

55. Occasions suitable for Concomitant Measurements

IN the preceding chapters we have been principally concerned with the means whereby experimental precision may be increased through the knowledge that groups of material may be selected, the parts of which are more homogeneous than are the different groups. We have been using such facts as that animals more nearly related by blood are generally more alike than animals less nearly related, that men of the same race or district are likely to be more similar than men of different races, that plots of land resemble one another more nearly in fertility the closer together they lie, or that apparatus supplied by the same manufacturer will generally be more nearly comparable than the makes supplied by different firms. It has been shown that very great increases in precision are possible by utilising these and analogous facts, even when the amount of material which is closely homogeneous with any chosen unit is extremely limited, provided that within this limitation we may assign the treatments to be tested at will so as to build up a comprehensive experiment.

There is a second means by which precision may, in appropriate cases, be much increased by the elimination of causes of variation which cannot be controlled, which has the advantage of being applicable when we cannot exercise a free choice in the distribution of the treatments. For example, in a feeding experiment with animals, where we are concerned to measure their response to a number of different rations or diets, we may often be able to ensure that the animals entering on the treatments to be tested shall be of the same age, and often, also, that they shall be closely related, or of the same parentage. But such groups of closely related animals as are available will not, at the same age, have attained exactly to the same size, as measured by weight, or in any other appropriate manner. If we decide that they shall enter the experiment at the same age, it may well be that the differences in initial weight constitute an uncontrolled cause of variation among the responses to treatment, which will sensibly diminish the precision of the comparisons. If the animals are assigned at random to the different treatments, either absolutely or subject to restrictions of the kinds which have been discussed, the differences in initial weight will not, of course, vitiate the tests of significance, for, though they may contribute to the error of our comparisons, they will then also contribute in due measure to the estimates of error by which the significance of these comparisons are to be judged. They may, however, constitute an element of error which it is desirable, and possible, to eliminate. The possibility arises from the fact that, without being equalised, these differences of initial weight may none the less be measured. Their effects upon our final results may approximately be estimated, and the results adjusted in accordance with the estimated effects, so as to afford a final precision, in many cases, almost as great as though complete equalisation had been possible.

Similar situations frequently arise in other fields of work. In agricultural experiments involving the yield following different kinds of treatments, it may be apparent that the yields of the different plots have been much disturbed by variations in the number of plants which have established themselves. If we are satisfied that this variation in plant number is not itself an effect of the treatments being investigated, or if we are willing to confine our investigation to the effects on yield, excluding such as flow directly or indirectly from effects brought about by variations in plant number, then it will appear desirable to introduce into our comparisons a correction which makes allowance, at least approximately, for the variations in yield directly due to variation in plant number itself. In introducing such a correction it is important to make sure that our procedure shall not in any way invalidate the test of significance to be applied to the comparisons, and thought will often be required to assure ourselves that the effects eliminated shall really be only those which are irrelevant to the aim of the experiment.

Again, let us suppose that a number of remedial treatments are to be tested on an orchard or plantation, the trees of which show in varying measure the effects of disease. It might be possible to grade the individual plants prior to the application of the treatments, and to apply the treatments to equal numbers of plants showing each grade of injury. But this would not always be possible, especially if it is not to individual plants but to small plots, each containing several plants, that the remedial measures must be applied. Such a procedure would also, in any case, necessarily sacrifice the advantage of propinquity of the areas which it is desired to compare. To meet this difficulty it is open to us to apply the different treatments to plots random-ised and adequately replicated, but chosen without regard to the initial grade of injury of the plants they contain. The grades of injury of these plants may, however, be recorded both initially and finally, when the treatments may be supposed to have exerted such effects as they are capable of, and the comparison of the final condition of the plots which have received different treatments may be adjusted to take account of the degrees of injury initially shown by these same plots.

With perennial plantations the same principle may very advantageously be applied to studies of the effects of manuring, pruning, and other variable treatments, on the yield. Yield in such cases is evidently much influenced, not only by variations in soil fertility, but also by the individual capacities of different plants, which, whether hereditary or not, persist from year to year. Records of the yield of individual rubber trees, or of small areas of tea-plantation, thus show large and relatively permanent differences. In such cases records of yield for a preliminary period under uniform treatment provide a most valuable guide in interpreting the records after the treatments have been varied. It would in these cases be possible to choose areas for the different treatments such that their previous record was approximately equalised. But to do so is usually troublesome, inexact, and unnecessary. Moreover, as the plots so chosen cannot also be arranged in compact blocks, or in other advantageous arrangements, such as the Latin square, the loss of precision due to sacrificing this advantage is often considerable. It is now usual, therefore, to arrange the plots in some way which is topographically advantageous, irrespective of their previous records, and to utilise the information supplied by these as an adjustment or correction to the subsequent yields measured under varying treatments. It may be noted, however, that with annual agricultural crops, knowledge of the yields of the experimental area in a previous year under uniform treatment has not been found sufficiently to increase the precision to warrant the adoption of such uniformity trials as a preliminary to projected experiments. Such a procedure necessarily nearly doubles the experimental labour, and as it is not found to double the amount of information supplied by the experiment but to increase it, perhaps by 50 per cent., it is clearly unprofitable. For, by the application of twice the expenditure in time and money in the experimental year, the amount of information recovered may with confidence be expected to be approximately doubled. Consequently, on grounds of precision alone, such preliminary trials with annual crops are not to be recommended. The fact that they entail at least a year's delay in the experimental results adds to the force of this conclusion.

In many cases it may be possible to take two or more concomitant measurements, each of which severally may be expected, when proper allowance is made for it, to increase the precision of the comparisons to be made, and which, if used jointly, may increase them still further. Thus, if groups of school children be supplied, in addition to their home diet, with a ration of milk, either raw or pasteurised, children in the same school may be assigned properly at random to the groups receiving these different additions to their diet. With large numbers of subjects the age distributions of the two groups may be very nearly equalised, but with the smaller numbers attending a particular school such equalisation of age will necessarily be somewhat inexact, and, apart from age, it is certain that the two groups of children will differ somewhat in the initial height and weight. The variations in these initial values, moreover, may all be suspected of having, possibly, an appreciable influence on the apparent response to the nutrients as measured by increments in height or weight. The most thorough procedure for such a case would be to eliminate, or make allowance for, all these three variables jointly; and, though it might not in fact be necessary to take account of more than two, or of even one of them, we could only assure ourselves that such a simpler procedure was in reality effective by examining the effects of making allowance for all three jointly.

56. Arbitrary Corrections

In the examples outlined above, in which an observable but uncontrolled concomitant might reasonably be expected, if proper account can be taken of it, to add to the precision of the results, it is still a common practice to introduce corrections arrived at *a priori*, without reference to what the data themselves have to tell of the amount of the corrections to be applied. Thus in a feeding experiment with animals it might be thought proper to take account of the variation in their initial weights by calculating the responses of different individuals, not by their absolute increases in weight, but by their increase relative to their initial weight, or as percentage increases. Equally, in allowing for the effect of variation in plant number upon an agricultural yield it is possible, and has sometimes been thought appropriate, to calculate the yield per plant in place of the yield per unit area, as the measure of the efficacy of the treatments to be compared. In judging of the effects of treatments on the grade of visible damage caused by disease it might be thought sufficient to compare the differences between the average grades of the different plants receiving any treatment, before and after that treatment has been applied, in order to allow for the fact that the areas differently treated, though assigned properly at random, were not initially in exactly the same condition. When allowing for the differences between different plots observed in a preliminary trial of a plantation, either the proportional system, or that dependent on simple differences, might equally be advocated, and would, perhaps, not give greatly different results.

Such methods of discounting *a priori* the effects of concomitant variates, so utilising them to increase the precision of experimental comparisons, should not be rejected as invalid, even though we may know that the suppositions on which they are based are experimentally untrue. The experimenter, for example, has a perfect right to measure the efficiency of different feeding stuffs, either by the average percentage increase of different animals, or by the average absolute increase, as he pleases, and, with a properly designed experiment, he will ascertain whether the materials tested do or do not give significantly different results as measured in these alternative ways.   He has this right, none the less, even if experiments with a uniform feeding mixture, and animals of varying initial weight, have shown that the increments in weight during the experiment period neither are independent of initial weight nor are proportional to it.   What such experiments would make clear is that, for the purpose of detecting differences between the feeding stuffs tested, with the greatest possible precision in relation to the size of the trial, neither method of measuring weight increase is ideal, and that both are capable of some improvement.   If, for example, in experiments in the course of which the average weight of the animals had doubled, it was found that an initial difference in weight of 1 lb. was followed at the end of the experiment by a difference on the average of $1\frac{1}{2}$ lbs., it is obvious that an allowance on this scale would be preferable, for the purpose of

comparing different feeding stuffs, either to an allowance of a pound for a pound, as is the effect of taking
simple weight increases without regard to the initial
weight, or to an allowance of 2 lbs. for 1 lb., which would
be approximately the effect of judging the experimental
results by the proportional increases in weight.

Preliminary investigations of the correct allowance
to make for concomitant variates are usually wanting,
and are, fortunately, not a practical necessity, for the
results of a replicated experiment may themselves be
used to supply what is wanted. Let us suppose that
five feeding stuffs are to be tested, each on ten pigs,
the animals being assigned to the different rations
entirely at random. The average initial weights of
the groups assigned to the different feeding stuffs will
therefore vary somewhat by chance, though this variation will not be so great as the variation between the
initial weights of the different animals receiving the same
feeding stuff. The assignment being at random in
fact gives an assurance that the average differences
between the different lots of ten shall be smaller than
the individual differences in the ratio $1 : \sqrt{10}$ or, in
fact, should be rather less than one-third as great. A
direct comparison, within the groups receiving the same
mixture, of the extent to which greater initial weight is
followed by greater final weight, will, therefore, generally supply an estimate of the true allowance to be
made of amply sufficient accuracy for the small adjust-
ments which are to be based upon it. Moreover, such
an allowance based on the very same data to which
it is to be applied, is generally preferable to one based
on other experiments, even if these are much more
extensive, since it is certain that the conditions in which
different experiments are made vary greatly, and in
many unknown and uncontrolled ways. We have no

assurance that the allowance appropriate to one set of conditions or to one type of material shall still be even approximately appropriate when the conditions and the material are varied. Consequently, even if the appropriate allowance for each concomitant variable had been previously ascertained by sufficiently extensive experimentation, it would still be advantageous to rely, in each particular case, on the internal evidence of the experiment in question. It may also be noted that by doing so the experiment conserves its property of being self-contained, and, therefore, adequate to supply genuinely independent testimony on any point in dispute, and that such complete independence is attenuated, if not lost, if extraneous data are introduced in the process of its interpretation.

57. Calculation of the Adjustment

The process of calculating the average apparent effect on the experimental value of the increase of one unit of the concomitant measurement is, in principle, extremely simple. Statistically, such values fall into the class of what are known as " regression coefficients," and the variety of methods, appropriate to calculating such regressions, forms an extensive subject, which is treated more fully in the author's book, *Statistical Methods for Research Workers*. To illustrate the principle used, the detailed working for a simple case will be given here, from which the reader who is unfamiliar with regressions will be able to see exactly what the calculation amounts to, though a fuller study would be needed to recognise how the operations should best be carried out in particular cases. We will suppose that five feeding mixtures are being tested in respect to the live weight increase produced by them, between fixed limits of age, on groups of ten pigs, assigned at random to each of the five mixtures. If no account whatever were to be taken of the initial weight (x), we might deal with the final weights (y) as follows :—The ten final weights for each treatment are added to give totals corresponding to each treatment (A, B, C, D, E), and divided by 10 to give the corresponding mean values (a, b, c, d, e). To judge of the significance of the differences between these totals, or between these means, we must make an estimate of the magnitude of the variations due to uncontrolled causes, including initial weight, and this we may do by examining the variation in final weight among pigs fed with the same mixture. Each set of ten pigs treated alike will supply 9 degrees of freedom for this purpose, or 45 degrees of freedom in all, for the estimation of error. The sum of squares, corresponding to each 9 degrees of freedom, is found by squaring the ten final weights, adding the squares and deducting Aa, the product of the total and mean weight for the treatment concerned. The sum of squares corresponding to the 4 degrees of freedom for variance among treatments is likewise obtained by adding together the products of means and totals for the several treatments, and deducting the product of the grand total and the general mean, $i.e.$ by

$$Aa+Bb+Cc+Dd+Ee-Mm ;$$

where M stands for the grand total, and m for the general mean. The analysis of variance is thus of the simple form :—

TABLE 28

	Degrees of Freedom.
Treatments	4
Error .	45
Total .	49

Obviously, an exactly similar analysis can be made of the initial weights (x), though this is of no direct experimental interest. To do so is, however, the first step to take in utilising the values x in order to adjust the final weights (y) in making a closer comparison of the responses to different feeding mixtures. The next step is to make a third table of the same kind, utilising now, at each stage, instead of squares, the products of the numbers x and y. Thus, for each set of 9 degrees of freedom recognised as error, we take the product of the initial and final weight of each individual pig, add the products for the ten pigs treated alike, and deduct the product of the initial total and the final mean, or, what comes to the same thing, of the initial mean and the final total. We thus have a sum of products for the 45 degrees of freedom ascribed to error, comparable in every respect with the sum of squares belonging to the same degrees of freedom for the initial weights, or for the final weights. Equally, for the 4 degrees of freedom ascribed to treatments we may find the appropriate sum of products by multiplying the initial total weight for any treatment by the final mean weight, adding the five products so obtained and deducting the initial total weight of all the pigs, multiplied by their final mean weight.

The three corresponding tables derived from the squares of the final weights, the squares of the initial weights and the products of the two series, contain all that is needed for the adjustment of the final weight, and for the further study of the adjusted values. In particular, the appropriate adjustment to be subtracted from each final weight to allow for each additional pound in initial weight, as judged from the internal evidence of the experiment, by a comparison among pigs treated alike, is found simply by dividing the error term of the sum of products by the corresponding term in the sum of squares of initial weights.

This procedure is of quite general application. If, for example, the experiment had been of a more intricate design we might have chosen sets of five pigs each, from ten different litters, and assigned one pig of each litter to each treatment, so that the treatments should be tried on animals of more nearly equal genetic constitution than if a lot of fifty had been distributed wholly at random. The analysis would then have taken the form

TABLE 29

	Degrees of Freedom.
Litters	9
Treatments	4
Error	36
Total . . .	49

The differences between litters being thus eliminated from the experiment, both in the effects of treatment and in the estimation of error, we should in consequence derive the adjustment by dividing the error component of the sum of products by the corresponding component in the sum of squares in initial weights, because it is now only the relation between initial and final weight among pigs of the same litter that is wanted in adjusting the results. We may, therefore, in all cases obtain the empirical adjustment, indicated by the particular results of the experiment, by dividing the error component of the sum of products by that of the sum of squares of the concomitant observation.

In cases in which it is desired to make allowance simultaneously for two or more concomitant measurements, separate analyses in the same form should be made for each of these, and for the sum of products of each with the dependent variate to be adjusted, and with each other. The error terms of these tables will then provide a system of two or more linear equations in accordance with the general procedure of partial regression, the solutions of which represent the average effects of unit changes in the several independent variates. The principle of the adjustment is thus exactly the same whether we have to do with one concomitant variate or with many, and the use of two or more such concomitants involves no unmanageable increase in the labour of computation. The limiting factor in the utility of concomitant observations lies rather in the labour of additional measurements, which may not, even when the best possible use is made of them, lead to so great an increase in precision as could be obtained by increasing the size of the experiment on a simpler plan, or, in other ways, by the expenditure of an equivalent amount of time and attention. In cases, however, as with the initial weights of experimental animals, where the measurement to be used as a concomitant is one which would not in any case be omitted, the precision which can be gained by a direct evaluation of their actual effects is entirely profitable to the experiment.

58. The Test of Significance

We have now to evaluate this gain in precision so that the significance of the responses to different treatments may be tested after adjustment. Since the adjustment has been obtained from the error term we may regard 1 of the degrees of freedom ascribed to error as having been utilised in evaluating it. Supposing, that is, that only one concomitant variate has been used, and therefore only one coefficient has been evaluated. In general, the number of degrees of freedom utilised is equal to the number of concomitant variates. After allowing, therefore, for the initial weights of the animals in our experiment there will remain only 44 degrees of freedom for the estimation of error if the animals have been assigned wholly at random, and only 35 degrees of freedom if they have been assigned at random within the litters. The deduction to be made from the sum of squares ascribed to error in the analysis of the final weights due to the removal of this 1 degree of freedom, is easily calculated. It consists of the square of the error component in the analysis of covariance, divided by the error component of the analysis of variance of the initial weights. After deducting this portion the sum of squares ascribed to error may be divided by the degrees of freedom, to obtain the mean square appropriate to testing the significance of differences among the adjusted final weights. This use is entirely appropriate only if, as should be the case in a properly randomised experiment, the differences among the mean initial weights of the different groups of animals are small compared with the differences amongst animals of the same group from which the adjustment has been evaluated. If this were not so, the adjusted values would in some measure be also affected by the errors of estimation of the value of the adjustment applied. It is therefore a useful resource to apply a test of significance to the adjusted values, or any component of them of special interest, which shall take full account of the inexactitude of our estimate. We may illustrate the procedure for the case in which sets of five pigs from ten different litters have been assigned at random to the five feeding mixtures.

In this case 9 degrees of freedom representing differences between litters have been eliminated from the experimental comparisons, and from the estimate of error. With these we are no longer concerned. The sum of squares corresponding to the 35 degrees of freedom for the estimation of error, after adjustment, has been evaluated by means of deducting the square of a term from the analyses of covariance, divided by the corresponding term in the analysis of variance of the initial yields. The same process is now applied using the sum of the components for treatment and error from the same tables. This gives us the sum of squares corresponding to 39 degrees of freedom, for 1 has been deducted from the 40 originally available. Subtracting now the portion obtained for error, the difference represents the 4 degrees of freedom ascribable to treatments, after exact allowance has been made for the sampling error of the coefficient used in their adjustment. The sum of squares for these 4 degrees of freedom may therefore be compared with that for the 35 degrees of freedom due to error, as in an ordinary analysis of variance, in which no concomitant variate has been eliminated. The sum of squares ascribed to treatment by this method will be found to be somewhat less than the corresponding value derived from the adjusted means and totals, although these adjusted values are the best available from the experiment, only because a calculable portion of the variance among them is ascribable to the sampling error of the estimated rate of allowance, which portion it is proper to remove in making an exact test of the significance of the variation observed. In cases where the concomitant variation has not been properly randomised, the omission of this precaution may lead to serious errors, but in such cases the possibility of testing significance accurately is always questionable.

58·1. Missing Values

It sometimes happens, in an experiment in which some cause of disturbance has been carefully equalised, as are the rows and columns in a Latin square, that, by some unforeseen accident, one of the experimental values is missing. This may happen through the death of an individual, injury to a portion of a growing crop, a gross error in recording, or to any such cause. Without the missing value equalisation is no longer complete, and it is sometimes thought that the whole experiment has been wasted. Indeed, the possibility of such mishaps has been held to be a reason for avoiding all experiments having intricate or complex structures. The technique applicable to concomitant observations does not, however, rest upon any assumption of equalisation, and may be used to recover the information available in the values that remain. The experiment so repaired will not, of course, be so good as if it had not been injured; but there is no reason to suppose that the loss of information suffered will be disproportionate to the value of the experiment as a whole.

Instead of estimating an adjustment based on a regression coefficient, it is convenient to estimate the missing value itself. The principle employed is simply to insert an algebraic symbol (x) for the missing value. The ordinary process of analysis of variance will then yield not wholly numerical expressions for the sums of squares, but algebraic expressions quadratic in x. If, for example, the sum of squares for error is

$$A - 2Bx + Cx^2,$$

this will be minimised for the value,

$$x = \frac{B}{C}$$

which is the required estimate of the missing observation. For this value of x, the sum of squares ascribable to error is

$$A - \frac{B^2}{C}$$

which corresponds to a number of degrees of freedom

one less than would have been available had no value been missing.

It will be noticed that the coefficients of x^2 in the different lines of the analysis are all positive, and correspond with the analysis of variance of the concomitant observation, while the coefficients of $-2x$ correspond with the analysis of covariance. As in the case of concomitant measurements, where allowance must be made for the sampling error of the regression, the results of inserting the estimated value are not so accurate as if that value had actually been observed ; nevertheless, an unbiased test of significance may be made by minimising the sum of squares for the total of errors and treatments, and from this minimised value subtracting the minimised value for error only.

The reader is advised to practise this procedure, using such an example as that shown in Table 9, omitting any one of the 36 values there given. If more than one value is omitted, there will be two or more unknowns, and the process of minimising the sum of squares will yield as many equations, analogous to the simultaneous equations in partial regression.

It is instructive also to follow through algebraically the process given above, *e.g.* to show that when a single value is missing from a 6×6 Latin square,

(*a*) the reconstructed value is

$$\frac{1}{20}(6R'+6C'+6T'-2M)$$

when R', C' and T' are the incomplete totals for row, column and treatment from which the observation was missing, and M is the incomplete total of all observations.

(*b*) The sum of squares ascribable to treatments in testing significance is

$$\frac{1}{6}S(T-\overline{T})^2 + \frac{1}{100}(5T'+R'+C'-M)^2$$

M

where T stands for the total of any of the completely observed treatments, and T̄ for the mean of these totals. Evidently, the value lost has not affected the precision of comparisons among these treatments, representing 4 degrees of freedom. The second term gives the comparison of the incompletely recorded treatment with the mean of the other five.

59. Practical Examples

In Table 29·1 the pairs of numbers are the initial and final weights (after 12 weeks) of four groups of Northumbrian sheep, treated respectively with A nothing, B phenothiazine, C minerals and D both phenothiazine

TABLE 29·1

Initial and Final Weights in lbs. of Experimental Sheep
(W. Lyle Stewart's data)

A.		B.		C.		D.	
57,	94	46,	80	45,	70	38,	79
54,	84	40,	68	55,	90	59,	100
43,	81	36,	62	49,	80	45,	72
58,	87	40,	79	37,	58	44,	77
44,	70	49,	79	49,	82	47,	75
42,	67	50,	79	52,	91	52,	95
38,	78	44,	86	43,	79	37,	66
54,	71	44,	70	63,	84	49,	90
54,	80	44,	75	56,	96	38,	83
47,	63	42,	79	28,	59	33,	59
51,	90	45,	68	44,	69	65,	106
52,	86	43,	80	49,	90	35,	61
47,	79	42,	77	47,	79	41,	79
56,	79	44,	74	45,	74	43,	73
44,	74	54,	84	40,	70	41,	74
50,	82	43,	77	40,	62	41,	85
34,	56	46,	70	39,	71	47,	85
30,	49	31,	67	35,	62	51,	91
31,	28	41,	70	48,	84	48,	84
32,	58					31,	66
918, 1456		824, 1424		864, 1450		885, 1600	

and minerals. Analyse the variance and covariance of initial and final weights, within and between groups, and compare the average final weights after allowance for variations in initial weight.

Table 30 shows the arrangement of an experiment, carried out in sugar-beet, at Good Easter, Chelmsford, in 1932, by the National Institute of Agricultural Botany. Three varieties, a, b and c, are tested in combination with eight manurial mixtures, respectively containing and lacking sulphate of ammonia, at the rate of 0·6 cwt. of nitrogen per acre, superphosphate at the rate of 0·5 cwt. P_2O_5 per acre, and chloride of potash at the rate of 0·75 cwt. K_2O per acre. The twenty-four combinations of the three varieties with the eight manurings are arranged in four randomised blocks in the order shown. In each plot the first number is the number of plants lifted, while the second is the weight in pounds of washed roots.

In carrying out the analysis it should be observed that the varieties show significant differences in plant number, so that the yields in root weight adjusted for plant number will not necessarily represent varietal differences in yield under any uniform system of field treatment, but should represent yield differences for equal plant establishment.

When variation in plant number is not large a proportional allowance, based on a simple regression coefficient, is often entirely adequate. Theoretically, however, we should not expect the relationship between yield and plant number to be represented by a straight line over a wide range, but rather by a curve, having a maximum within or outside the range of the observations. To deal with curved regression, when it seems to be advantageous, it is only necessary to introduce not only the plant number but its square also as a second

TABLE 30

Arrangement, Plant Number and Yield, of Combined Manurial and Varietal Experiment with Sugar-beet
(Rothamsted Experimental Station Report, 1932)

I.		II.		III.		IV.	
cnp	103,112	bnp	142,150	anpk	107,139	ap	109,162
cn	121,118	anpk	147,155	a	114,127	bpk	143,139
ank	134,112	c	138,132	c	119,123	ck	129,151
bk	156,117	cn	141,152	cp	127,120	anpk	148,192
ak	131,152	cpk	126,115	bnp	133,118	bn	159,174
cpk	129,140	ap	134,175	cn	127,149	bp	120,143
cp	123,118	bnk	142,144	an	127,168	ak	145,188
bnpk	146,144	bn	138,159	anp	119,157	bnp	138,157
b	145,133	bpk	145,132	bn	140,166	a	127,158
an	136,184	cnp	144,175	bnpk	138,155	cpk	142,152
bnp	140,168	apk	133,158	b	139,138	cnp	143,173
cnk	126,148	ank	156,193	cpk	129,130	anp	132,193
bp	152,140	b	147,130	cnpk	129,173	bk	147,147
bnk	136,143	cp	139,142	cnk	107,147	cp	124,138
bn	124,163	bp	138,101	bnk	133,142	cn	127,165
a	124,162	cnpk	125,160	ak	130,141	ank	138,191
c	113,122	ak	161,164	ck	118,142	bnpk	140,153
cnpk	120,162	an	134,178	ap	134,142	b	127,128
anpk	120,175	a	133,162	bp	125,124	an	139,199
apk	126,140	bnpk	135,160	bpk	125,132	cnpk	137,185
anp	132,190	cnk	128,152	cnp	102,152	apk	132,160
ap	115,173	bk	152,137	bk	107,121	c	127,146
ck	91,107	ck	149,171	apk	106,148	bnk	148,159
bpk	137,127	anp	104,166	ank	101,171	cnk	110,136

concomitant observation, and to treat these exactly as though they were two independent variables. The fact that one of these may be calculated from the other does not in any respect interfere with their use in this way, and, of course, in special cases, the same principle may be used to introduce more complicated curves. Sound judgment as to the probable value of such elaborations, in comparison with the work required, can only be gained by trying them on bodies of actual observations, such as those shown in the table.

REFERENCES AND OTHER READING

R. A. FISHER (1925-1948). Statistical methods for research workers. Chap. V., §§ 25-29 ; Chap. VIII., § 49·1.

T. EDEN (1931). The experimental errors of field experiments with tea. Journal of Agricultural Science, xxi. 547-573.

Rothamsted Experimental Station Annual Report (1932).

H. G. SANDERS (1930). A note on the value of uniformity trials for subsequent experiments. Journal of Agricultural Science, xx. 63-73.

X

THE GENERALISATION OF NULL HYPOTHESES.
FIDUCIAL PROBABILITY

60. Precision regarded as Amount of Information

THE foregoing Chapters, III. to IX., have been devoted to cases to which the theory of errors is appropriate; that is to say, to cases in which the experimental result sought is found by testing the significance of the deviations shown by the observations, from a null hypothesis of a particular kind. In this kind of hypothesis all discrepancies classified as error, and not eliminated from our comparisons by equalisation or regression, are due to variation, in the material examined, following the normal law of errors with a definite and constant, but unknown, variance.

Granting the appropriateness of null hypotheses of this kind, our purpose has been to diminish the magnitude of the error components in the comparisons, and a number of devices have been illustrated by which this can be done, while at the same time the requirement can be satisfied that the experiment shall supply a valid estimate of the magnitude of the residual errors, by which the comparisons are still affected. In general, it has been seen that, with repeated experimentation on like material, the variance ascribable to error falls off inversely to the number of replications, so that in measuring the effectiveness of methods of reducing the error, an appropriate scale is provided by the inverse of the variance, or the *invariance*, as it is sometimes called, of the averages determined by the experiment.

If, therefore, any such average is determined with a sampling variance V, we may define a quantity I such that $I = 1/V$, and I will measure the quantity of information supplied by the experiment in respect of the particular value to which the variance refers. Information, of course, like other quantities, may be measured in units of different sizes, according to the subject under discussion. Thus, with agricultural yields it is convenient to consider an experiment giving a standard error of 10 per cent. as supplying one unit of information. One giving a standard error of only 5 per cent. will, therefore, supply four units. An experiment with a standard error of 2 per cent. will yield twenty-five, and one with a standard error of 1 per cent. will yield a hundred of such units. The amount of information is thus measurable on a scale inverse to the variance, or inverse to the square of the standard error.

One immediate consequence of this method of evaluation is that when an experimental programme is enlarged by simple repetition on like material, the amount of information gained is proportional to the labour and expense incurred. Consequently, we may ascertain the cost, per unit of information gained, of any type of experimentation of which we have adequate experience ; or, if we wish, we may so use the data from any single large experiment. The cost of attaining any desired level of precision, or of gaining any desired amount of information by the same method is thus easily calculable. What is also important, the relative costliness of different methods of experimentation may be directly compared, and the saving effected by improved methods of design, or by the use of concomitant observations, may be given an entirely objective and tangible value.

In such calculations it is appropriate that the items of labour and skilled supervision chargeable to a particular method of experimentation shall be fairly and carefully recorded and calculated. For any time and labour devoted to experimental work must be regarded as having been diverted from other work of scientific value, to which they might otherwise have been given. Even rough costings of this kind will usually show that the efficiency with which limited resources can be applied is capable of relatively enormous increases by careful planning of the experimental programme, and there is nothing in the nature of scientific work which requires that the allocation of the resources to the ends aimed at should be in any degree rougher, or less scrupulous, than in the case of a commercial business. The waste of scientific resources in futile experimentation has, in the past, been immense in many fields. One important cause at least of this waste has been a failure to utilise past experience in evaluating the precision attainable by an experiment of given magnitude, and in planning to work on a scale sufficient to give a practically useful result.

A serious consequence of the neglect to make systematically estimates of the efficiency of different methods of experimentation is the danger that satisfactory methods, or methods which with further improvement are capable of becoming satisfactory, may be overlooked, or discarded, in favour of others enjoying a temporary popularity. Fashions in scientific research are subject to rapid changes. Any brilliant achievement, on which attention is temporarily focused, may give a prestige to the method employed, or to some part of it, even in applications to which it has no special appropriateness. The teaching given in universities to future research workers is often particularly unbalanced in this respect, possibly because the university teacher cannot give his whole time to the study of the practical aspects of research problems, possibly because he unwittingly emphasises the importance of the particular procedures with which he is best acquainted.

61. Multiplicity of Tests of the same Hypothesis

The concept of quantity of information is applicable to types of experimentation and of observational programmes other than those for which the theory of errors supplies the appropriate null hypotheses. Before considering these, as will be done in the following chapter, it is advisable to consider a somewhat more elaborate logical situation than that introduced in Chapter II. It was there pointed out that, in order to be used as a null hypothesis, a hypothesis must specify the frequencies with which the different results of our experiment shall occur, and that the interpretation of the experiment consisted in dividing these results into two classes, one of which is to be judged as opposed to, and the other as conformable with the null hypothesis. If these classes of results are chosen, such that the first will occur when the null hypothesis is true with a known degree of rarity in, for example, 5 per cent. or 1 per cent. of trials, then we have a test by which to judge, at a known level of significance, whether or not the data contradict the hypothesis to be tested.

We may now observe that the same data may contradict the hypothesis in any one of a number of different ways. For example, in the psycho-physical experiment (Chapter II.) it is not only possible for the subject to designate the cups correctly more often than would be expected by chance, but it is also possible that she may do so less often. Instead of using a test of significance which separates from the remainder a group of possible occurrences, known to have a certain small probability when the null hypothesis is true, and characterised by showing an excess of correct classifications, we might have chosen a test separating an equally infrequent group of occurrences of the opposite kind. The reason for not using this latter test is obvious, since the object of the experiment was to demonstrate, if it existed, the sensory discrimination of a subject claiming to be able to distinguish correctly two classes of objects. For this purpose the new test proposed would be entirely inappropriate, and no experimenter would be tempted to employ it. Mathematically, however, it is as valid as any other, in that with proper randomisation it is demonstrable that it would give a significant result with known probability, if the null hypothesis were true.

Again, in Darwin's experiment on growth rate discussed in Chapter III., it has been shown that the test of significance using " Student's " t is appropriate to the question with a view to which the experiment was carried out. Many other tests, however, less appropriate in this regard, or quite inappropriate, might have been applied to the data. Such tests may be made mathematically valid by ensuring that they each separate, for purposes of interpretation, a group of possible results of the experiment having a known and small probability, when the null hypothesis is true. For this purpose any quantity might have been calculated from the data, provided that its sampling distribution is completely determined by the null hypothesis, and any portion of the range of distribution of this quantity could be chosen as significant, provided that the frequency with which it falls in this portion of its range is ·05 or ·01, or whatever may be the level of significance chosen for the test.

Some such tests would be of no interest in any circumstances with which experimenters are familiar. Others, though not appropriate to the object Darwin had in view, might be appropriate to an experimenter studying a different subject. Thus, if the aim of the experiment had been, not to ascertain whether the average height of the cross-fertilised plants was, or was not, greater than that of the self-fertilised, but whether the difference in height between the cross- and self-fertilised plants of any pair was distributed normally, or in an unsymmetrical distribution, a valid test appropriate to this point could be devised. In addition to calculating, as in Chapter III., the sum of the squares of the deviations of these differences from their mean, we might calculate the sum of the cubes of these differences, having regard to their signs, and the ratio of the latter sum to the former raised to the power of $3/2$ may be shown, on the null hypothesis, to have a determinate distribution for a given number of pairs of plants. The exact form of this distribution is at present unknown, since the distributional problem here considered is not one of those that have been solved. Nothing, however, but lack of mathematical knowledge prevents us from stating exactly outside what limits the ratio must lie to have a given level of significance. This test would pick out as statistically significant quite different sets of experimental results from those selected by the t test. It is in no sense a substitute for that test, or suited to perform the same functions. It is designed to answer a different question, although in both cases the question is answered by selecting a group of possible experimental results deemed to contradict the same null hypothesis. They may properly be thought of as testing different features of this hypothesis. The hypothesis tested in both cases states that the distribution of differences in height is centred at zero and is normal in form. The one test is appropriate when we are interested especially in the possibility that it is not centred at zero. In this case the question of normality is, as has been shown, of quite trivial importance. The other is appropriate when we are interested in the possibility that the distribution is skew, or unsymmetrical about its mean, and in this case the value of the mean is entirely irrelevant.

The notion that different tests of significance are appropriate to test different features of the same null hypothesis presents no difficulty to workers engaged in practical experimentation, but has been the occasion of much theoretical discussion among statisticians. The reason for this diversity of view-point is perhaps that the experimenter is thinking in terms of observational values, and is aware of what observational discrepancy it is which interests him, and which he thinks may be statistically significant, before he enquires what test of significance, if any, is available appropriate to his needs. He is, therefore, not usually concerned with the question : To what observational feature should a test of significance be applied ? This question, when the answer to it is not already known, can be fruitfully discussed only when the experimenter has in view, not a single null hypothesis, but a class of such hypotheses, in the significance of deviations from each of which he is equally interested. We shall, later, discuss in more detail the logical situation created when this is the case. It should not, however, be thought that such an elaborate theoretical background is a normal condition of experimentation, or that it is needed for the competent and effective use of tests of significance.

62. Extension of the *t* Test

In hypotheses, based on the theory of errors, there is, however, one extension which is normally held in view, and which, for the great simplicity of its consequences, is well fitted to introduce the more complex situations in which methods of statistical estimation require to be discussed. In Chapter III. we illustrated " Student's " *t* test of significance with Darwin's data on the growth of young maize plants. The hypothesis to be tested was that the difference in height, between the cross-fertilised and the self-fertilised plant of the same pair, was distributed in some normal distribution about zero as its mean. We might, however, have considered a similar hypothesis, giving to the mean difference any other number, positive, negative, or fractional, of inches. If, instead of testing whether or not the mean could have been zero, we had chosen to test whether or not it had any unspecified value, μ, measured in eighths of an inch, then the deviation of our observed mean, 20·93, from the hypothetical value, μ, is

$$20 \cdot 93 - \mu$$

and this quantity, on the hypothesis to be tested, will be distributed normally about zero with a standard deviation, of which we have an estimate based on 14 degrees of freedom, the value of which is 9·746.

Consequently, if

$$t = \frac{20 \cdot 93 - \mu}{9 \cdot 746}$$

then *t* will be distributed in the distribution given by " Student " for 14 degrees of freedom, a distribution which is known with exactitude independently of the observations. We have the important logical situation, in which a quantity, t, having a sampling distribution known with precision, is expressible in terms of an unknown and hypothetical quantity, μ, together with other quantities known exactly by observation. We say known exactly, because the mathematical relations stated are true of the actual values derived from the observations, and not of the hypothetical values of which they might be regarded as estimates. Such actual values derived from the observation are distinguished by the term *statistics*, from the parameters, or hypothetical quantities introduced to specify the population sampled.

An important application, due to Maskell, is to choose the values of t appropriate to any chosen level of significance, and insert them in the equation. Thus t has a 5 per cent. chance of lying outside the limits $\pm 2 \cdot 145$. Multiplying this value by the estimated standard deviation, $9 \cdot 746$, we have $20 \cdot 90$ and may write

$$\mu = 20 \cdot 93 \pm 20 \cdot 90$$
$$= 0 \cdot 03, \text{ or } 41 \cdot 83$$

as the corresponding limits for the value of μ.

One familiar way of viewing this result is, that the experiment has provided an estimate, $20 \cdot 93$ eighths of an inch, of the average difference, μ, between the heights of two sorts of plants; that this estimate has a standard error $9 \cdot 746$, and that " Student's " distribution shows that, for 14 degrees of freedom, the 5 per cent. level of significance is reached when we pass outside the limits $\pm 2 \cdot 145$ times the standard error. An alternative view of the matter is to consider that variation of the unknown parameter, μ, generates a continuum of hypotheses each of which might be regarded as a null hypothesis, which the experiment is capable of testing. In this case the data of the experiment, and the test of significance based upon them, have divided this continuum into two portions. One, a region in which μ lies between the limits 0·03 and 41·83, is accepted by the test of significance, in the sense that values of μ within this region are not contradicted by the data, at the level of significance chosen. The remainder of the · continuum, including all values of μ outside these limits, is rejected by the test of significance.

It can now be seen that the t test is not only valid for the original null hypothesis that the mean difference is zero, but is particularly appropriate to an experimenter who has in view the whole set of hypotheses obtained by giving μ different values. The reason is that the two quantities, the sum and the sum of squares, calculated from the data together contain all the information supplied by the data concerning the mean and variance of the hypothetical normal curve. Statistics possessing this remarkable property are said to be *sufficient*, because no others can, in these cases, add anything to our information. The peculiarities presented by t, which give it its unique value for this type of problem, are :—

    (i) Its distribution is known with exactitude, without any supplementary assumptions or approximations.

    (ii) It is expressible in terms of the single unknown parameter, μ, together with known statistics only.

    (iii) The statistics involved in this expression are sufficient.

62·1. Fiducial Limits of a Ratio

The flexibility and directness of the fiducial argument is well illustrated by its application to find the fiducial limits of a ratio between quantities having normally distributed estimates. Galton, whom we quote on page 30, was interested in the ratio of the measurements of self-fertilised to cross-fertilised plants. He gives the ratio for maize as 84 per cent., though the totals of the fifteen pairs of plants given in his table, 2109 and 2423, in eighths of an inch, give a ratio 87 per cent. It is often convenient to the experimenter to state such ratios, and it is useful also to be able to state limits within which the true ratio probably lies.

In many cases, where the measurements are necessarily positive, it is satisfactory, though somewhat laborious, to make the test of the preceding section using the logarithms of all measurements in place of the measurements themselves. The difference between the logarithms of measurements of the same pair would be treated as normally distributed about some unknown mean, representing the true mean ratio. More generally, however, negative ratios are possible, and it is of more interest to consider the ratio of the true means rather than the logarithmic mean of the ratios. Instead of finding the fiducial limit of μ, by applying the t test to a set of quantities

$$x - y - \mu,$$

and finding the values of μ for which t has a given level of significance, we may instead apply the t test to the set of quantities

$$y - ax,$$

so that the fiducial limits of a, at, for example, the

5 per cent. level, are such as to make $t = 2.145$, for 14 degrees of freedom.

The total of the fifteen values of $y - ax$ will then be $2109 - 2423\,a$, and the term for the discrepancy between the means in the analysis of variance is

$$(2109 - 2423a)^2/15.$$

The sum of the squares of the deviations from their mean of the individual values of $y - ax$ is

$$3771 \cdot 6 + 2225 \cdot 8(2a) + 11721 \cdot 7\dot{3}(a^2) \; ;$$

a quadratic expression in which the coefficients are the sums of squares and products (with reversed sign) of the deviations from their means of the measurements of the self-fertilised and the cross-fertilised plants. If the first expression bears to the second the ratio $t^2/14$, then a must satisfy the quadratic equation

$$387543a^2 - 341405(2a) + 295286 = 0,$$

the roots of which,

$$a = \cdot99980 \text{ and } a = \cdot76209,$$

show that the data contradict, at the 5 per cent. level of significance, any statement of the form " The true average for self-fertilisation is the fraction a of the true average for cross-fertilisation," whenever a lies outside the limits $76 \cdot 209$ per cent. and $99 \cdot 980$ per cent. The fiducial probability that a lies between these limits is 95 per cent.

63. The χ^2 Test

What is meant by choosing a test of significance appropriate to a special purpose, may now be illustrated by considering what should be done if the experimenter were interested, not in whether the mean of the distribu-

N

tion could exceed a given value, or could lie in a given range, but in the value of the variance of the same distribution. What is now needed is a test of significance provided by a quantity (i) having a precisely known distribution, and (ii) expressible in terms of the unknown variance, ϕ, of the distribution sampled, together with sufficient statistics only.

Now, if χ^2/n is the ratio of the variance, as estimated from the sample for n degrees of freedom, to the true variance, ϕ, it is known that χ^2 is distributed, independently of the mean and variance of the population sampled, in a distribution which is known when n is known. If we wish to set a probable upper limit to the value of ϕ, we note that for $n = 14$, χ^2 is less than 6·571 * in only 5 per cent. of trials. Putting this value for χ^2 in the equation,

$$\chi^2 = \frac{19945}{\phi},$$

we have

$$\phi = 3035.$$

In other words, variances exceeding 3035, or standard deviations exceeding 55·09, are rejected at the 5 per cent. level of significance.

Equally, had we wished to set a probable lower limit to the value of ϕ we should have noted that χ^2 exceeds the value 23·685 in only 5 per cent. of trials. Consequently, the rejection of the 5 per cent. of values of χ^2 which are highest will exclude values of less than 19945/23·685, or 844. We may thus reject values of the variance below 844, or of the standard deviation below 29·06, at the 5 per cent. level of significance. If, however, we rejected values for the standard deviation

* For Table of χ^2 see *Statistical Methods for Research Workers*, Table III.

both below 29·06 and above 55·09, we should be
rejecting both of two sets of contingencies each having
a probability of 5 per cent., and so should be working,
not at the 5 per cent., but at the 10 per cent. level of
significance. If he wishes to work at the 5 per cent.
level, the experimenter has the choice, according to the
purpose of his researches,

  (i) of ascertaining an upper limit for the unknown
      variance without rejecting any lower values,
 (ii) of ascertaining a lower limit without rejecting
      any higher value, or
(iii) of ascertaining a pair of limits beyond which
      values are rejected, representing two fre-
      quencies totalling 5 per cent. together.

The tests appropriate for discriminating among a
group of hypothetical populations having different
variances are thus quite distinct from those appropriate
to discriminating among distributions having different
means. Within the limits of the theory of errors, the
mean and the variance are the only two quantities needed
to specify the hypothetical population. It is the circumstance that statistics sufficient for the estimation of
these two quantities are obtained merely from the sum
and the sum of squares of the observations, that gives
a peculiar simplicity to problems for which the theory
of errors is appropriate. This simplicity appears in an
alternative form of statement, which is legitimate in
these cases, namely, statements of the probability that
the unknown parameters, such as μ and ϕ, should lie
within specified limits. Such statements are termed
statements of *fiducial* probability, to distinguish them
from the statements of *inverse* probability, by which
mathematicians formerly attempted to express the
results of inductive inference. Statements of inverse

probability have a different logical content from statements of fiducial probability, in spite of their similarity of form, and require for their truth the postulation of knowledge beyond that obtained by direct observation.

In the discussion above of the results of Darwin's experiment, instead of saying that at the 5 per cent. level of significance we should reject hypothetical variances exceeding 3035, it would be equivalent to say that the fiducial probability is 5 per cent. that the variance should exceed 3035. Equally, the fiducial probability is 5 per cent. that it should be less than 844 ; consequently, it is 10 per cent. that it should lie outside the range between these two numbers. With respect to the mean, it may in the same way be said that it has a fiducial probability of 2½ per cent. of being less than 0·03, or of being greater than 41·83, and, in the same sense, a probability of 95 per cent. of lying within these fiducial limits.

64. Wider Tests based on the Analysis of Variance

In the more general type of problem, to which the z test is applicable, and in which we may have an analysis of the variance into a considerable number of subdivisions, we have a wide choice of tests of significance, each appropriate to answering a different question. Logically, these questions refer to the acceptance or rejection of different hypotheses or sets of hypotheses, and it will be useful to discuss them explicitly from this point of view. The practically useful variations are those which concern the hypothetical means of the different classes of observations which have been made.

As an example, let us consider the 6 × 6 Latin square, of which numerical observations were given in Chapter V. The arithmetical analysis obtained by the method there described is set out below.

TABLE 31

	Degrees of Freedom.	Sum of Squares.	Mean Square.	$\frac{1}{2}$ Log$_e$.
Rows	5	54,199	...	...
Columns . . .	5	24,467	...	...
Treatments . . .	5	248,180	49,636	1·9524
Error	20	30,541	1,527	0·2117
Total . .	35	357,387	...	1·7407

It will be seen that the value obtained for z was 1·7407. The 1 per cent. level for 5 degrees of freedom against 20 is ·7058. Consequently, the data very significantly contradict the hypothesis that all treatments were giving the same yield. We might, if it seemed appropriate, go further and say that if ζ stands for the true value of which z is an estimate, then all hypotheses which make ζ less than 1·0349 are contradicted by the data at the 1 per cent. level of significance. The hypothesis that the treatments do not affect the yield makes $\zeta = 0$. The wider hypothesis, that the yields produced by the different treatments are a random sample from a normal distribution, will provide an indeterminate positive value for ζ. If ζ were 1·0349 the mean square ascribed to treatments would be 7·923 times that ascribed to error. Since the mean square ascribed to treatments includes also the variability due to sampling error, the portion due to the effects of treatments themselves cannot be less than 6·923 times as great as the variance due to error in our estimates of the mean yields from the several treatments.

The mean square due to error has been found to be 1527, and this is the variance ascribable to error of a single plot. Dividing by 6, we find that the variance of the mean of six plots is 254·5. Multiplying this by

6·923 we have 1761·9 as the least admissible value for the variance due to treatments. The standard deviation corresponding to this variance is 41·97, or just over 9 per cent. of the mean yield, 462·75, observed in the experimental plots. It may be noticed that, apart from the inappropriateness, in the present instance, of the hypothesis that the *treatment* effects constitute a sample from a normal distribution, the calculation above departs from strict rigour in accepting the estimate of error based on 20 degrees of freedom, without making special allowance for the fact that this estimate is itself liable to sampling errors.

We have treated the experiment above as though nothing were known of the treatments applied, or as though these were regarded merely as causes disturbing the yields with an unknown variance. Actually, it is known that the treatments D, E, F differ from A, B, C in including an additional nitrogenous dressing, while A, B, C and, in like manner, D, E, F differ among themselves in receiving respectively 0, 1, 2 units of a phosphatic dressing. The 5 degrees of freedom ascribed to treatments are, therefore, not plausibly to be considered as homogeneous among themselves, but may properly be subdivided, as we have seen in previous chapters, into unitary elements of very different agricultural importance.

The total yields of the six treatments are set out below in relation to the manurial treatment received. The eighteen plots receiving the nitrogenous dressing exceed the remaining eighteen plots in yield by 1667, so that this degree of freedom, N, contributes $1667^2/36$ or 77,191, to the total of 248,180 ascribed to treatments. The second degree of freedom of primary importance, P_1, is found by subtracting the yield of the twelve plots without phosphate from that of the twelve plots with double phosphate. The difference is 1977, so that the contribution of this degree of freedom is $1977^2/24$, or 162,855. This is the primary effect of phosphate. The second degree of freedom of this ingredient, P_2, may be found by observing that the increment in the yield of twelve plots, due to a single application, is 1179, while

TABLE 32

	No Nitrogen.	Nitrogen.	Total.	Difference.
No phosphate . .	2070	2431	4501	361
Single phosphate . .	2559	3121	5680	562
Double phosphate .	2867	3611	6478	744
Total . .	7496	9163	16,659	1667

the additional increment due to the second application is 798. The difference is 381, and represents the excess of twice the yields for a single application over those for 0, or 2 units. The contribution of this degree of freedom is therefore $381^2/72$, or 2016. Similarly, using the differences between the yields with and without nitrogen, instead of the sums, we find for NP_1, $383^2/24 = 6112$, and for NP_2, $19^2/72 = 5$.

We are now at liberty to discuss the significance of each degree of freedom severally, and, because the experiment is a well-designed one, we shall find that to each corresponds a system of appropriate hypotheses relevant to the aims of the experiment. Thus, the 1 degree of freedom due to nitrogen has a mean square 50.56 times as great as that due to error. The value of " Student's " t is therefore about 7.110. The 5 per cent. value of t for 20 degrees of freedom is 2.086, so that at this level of significance we may exclude all hypotheses ascribing to the nitrogenous dressing less than $5 \cdot 024/7 \cdot 110$, or more than $9 \cdot 196/7 \cdot 110$ of the apparent benefit observed. This conclusion refers directly to the manurial comparison on which it is based, and is entirely independent of the other conclusions to be drawn from the experiment as to the effects of phosphate or of its interactions with nitrogen. Naturally, also, if there were no such interactions, the conclusion would be applicable at levels of phosphatic manuring other than those used in the experiment. The data here indicate that the return from nitrogen would be definitely higher with higher phosphatic dressings than those used. The inference as to the return with the actual phosphatic dressings used is, however, direct and independent of the interaction.

Each of the other elements into which the effects of treatments have been analysed may be treated independently, as we have treated N. A glance at the items of the expanded analysis of variance will show on which of these decisive evidence has been obtained.

TABLE 33

Component of Treatment.					Degrees of Freedom.	Mean Square.
N	.	.	.	.	1	77,191
P_1	.	.	.	.	1	162,855
P_2	.	.	.	.	1	2,016
NP_1	.	.	.	.	1	6,112
NP_2	.	.	.	.	1	5
			Total	.	5	248,179
			Error	.	20	1,527

Thus the primary effect of phosphate, like that of nitrogen, is demonstrated with unquestioned significance, and the magnitude of the return evaluated with fair accuracy. On the other hand, the contribution of the component NP_2 is much less than might have appeared as the result of random errors. The results are entirely compatible with the theoretical possibility that the response to nitrogen at different levels of phosphatic application changes in strict proportion to the amount of phosphate applied. The two remaining items, for P_2 and NP_1, are intermediate in magnitude, indicating that the evidence of the experiment on two corresponding modes of varying the null hypothesis is of an intermediate character. For P_2 the contribution, 2016, is statistically insignificant. The experiment does not prove that the additional response to the second dose of phosphatic manure is certainly less than that to the first. It is in fact less, in accordance with common agricultural experience, but the experiment could not suffice by itself to demonstrate the reality of this decrease. If we consider a series of hypotheses with different values for the diminishing return, and determine which of these values are compatible, at any given level of significance, with the observed yields, some of the values which would appear to be acceptable would be negative, *i.e.* would represent increasing returns, though in the greater part of the acceptable range positive values would prevail. Even if the test of significance were chosen, so as to determine not both limits, but the lower level only, this lower limit would be found to be negative. For t about 1·15, the fiducial probability of " increasing return " is about 13 per cent.

In the case of NP_1, which measures the extent to which the response to nitrogen is increased by an increased phosphatic dressing, the state of the evidence is somewhat different. The value of " Student's " t is 2·0004, while the value which is exceeded either positively or negatively in 5 per cent. of trials is 2·068. If, therefore, the experimenter had no more reason to expect an increasing than a decreasing response the observed value would have fallen just short of 5 per cent. significance. Since, however, normal agricultural experience would lead us to anticipate an increase, while a decrease would be somewhat anomalous, this test tells us not only that the observed magnitude of the effect is nearly significant, but also that it is in the right direction. These two independent pieces of evidence are combined by choosing a test, which determines a lower fiducial limit only, *i.e.* by taking for comparison the value of t, 1·725, tabulated as corresponding to the probability 10 per cent. This test shows that, at the 5 per cent. level of significance, any hypothesis which gives to the increase, in response to nitrogen, a negative value is contradicted by the experimental results, or, in other words, that a positive effect is demonstrated, at this level of significance, by the experiment. As in other cases, where an effect is little more than barely significant, the precision with which its value is estimated is, of course, extremely low.

It would have been legitimate to choose other comparisons among the treatments employed, and to make with them other tests of significance. We might, for example, have compared the plots receiving double directly with those receiving single phosphate, and have discussed the significance of this difference, in isolation from the other experimental results. The only inconvenience of such a course is that if, as is usually the case, the result is to be used in the examination of scientific theory, in the framing of practical advice, or in the designing of future experiments, in conjunction with facts of the same kind as the remainder of the experiment provides, it is clearly preferable that the whole of these should be recognised by means of a series of independent tests, each having some agricultural relevance. Although a series of tests can always be chosen, independent of the one with which we may start, the supplementary information provided by them

will often be of too complicated a kind for its bearing
on our effective conclusions to be readily appreciated.
Consequently, it will usually be preferable, as in the
example chosen, to design the experiment so as
to lead uniquely to a single series of tests chosen in
advance.

Where a number of independent tests of significance
have been made, on data from the same experiment,
each test allowing of the rejection of the true hypotheses
in 5 per cent. of trials, it follows that a hypothesis
specifying all the differences in yield between the treatments tested will, although true, be rejected with a
higher frequency. If, therefore, it were desired to
examine the possible variations of any hypothesis
which specified all these differences simultaneously
while maintaining the 5 per cent. level of significance,
a different procedure should be adopted. Actually, in
biology or in agriculture, it is seldom that the hypothetical
background is so fully elaborated that this is necessary.
It is therefore usually preferable to consider the
experiment, as we have done above, as throwing light
upon a number of theoretically independent questions.
There is however no difficulty, when required, in
making a comprehensive test on all questions simultaneously, as in the z test first employed, or in extending
this test so as to specify the aggregate of compound
hypotheses which are contradicted by the experiment
at any assigned level of significance.

In analysing the 5 degrees of freedom ascribable
to treatments in the 6×6 Latin square, certain differences
were obtained from the experimental yields, such as
the 1667 units of yield by which the plots receiving
nitrogen exceeded the remainder. Any hypothesis
respecting the difference in yield of the six treatments
used may be specified by the hypothetical values which

it gives corresponding to these observed differences. Thus if a_1 were the hypothetical value corresponding to 1667, a_2 corresponding to 1977, and so on, the sum of squares for the 5 degrees of freedom representing the deviations of the observed responses to treatments from those predicted by hypothesis would be

$$\frac{(1667-a_1)^2}{36} + \frac{(1977-a_2)^2}{24} + \frac{(381-a_3)^2}{72}$$

$$+ \frac{(383-a_4)^2}{24} + \frac{(19-a_5)_2}{72}$$

We may now find how large this expression must be in order that z should be equal to its 1 per cent. value. This value as given by the table is 0·7058. Adding to this $\frac{1}{2}$ log$_e$ for error, ·2117, we have ·9175 corresponding to a mean square 6265, or to a sum of squares 31,325. The 1 per cent. test of significance for a hypothesis specifying all the values a_1, a_2, . . ., a_5 will therefore reject any hypothesis for which the quadratic expression set out above exceeds 31,325, and will accept all hypotheses for which it has a lower value.

65. Comparisons with Interactions

The last class of variation to be considered in the tests of significance derivable from the analysis of variance consists of cases in which we compare primary effects with interactions, or interactions with interactions of a higher order. If, for example, a test were carried out of five varieties of an agricultural plant, using a Latin square laid down at each of ten representative farms, in a region to which the five varieties tested have all some claim to be thought appropriate, the experiment at each farm will provide an analysis of the form :

TABLE 34

	Degrees of Freedom.
Rows	4
Columns	4
Varieties	4
Error	12
Total . .	24

If we have corresponding data for each of ten places the whole series will yield together 40 degrees of freedom for rows and 40 degrees for columns, all of which represent components of heterogeneity which have been eliminated. There will also be 120 degrees of freedom in all for error. But the remaining 40, composed of the components ascribed to variety at each of the ten places, is divisible into 4 degrees of freedom for variety V, and 36 for interaction between variety and place VP. There would, of course, also be 9 degrees of freedom, representing the contrast between places, but with these we are not concerned. The complete analysis of such a record of 250 yields would therefore be as follows :—

TABLE 35

	Degrees of Freedom.
Rows	40
Columns	40
Places	9
Varieties	4
V × P	36
Error	120
Total .	249

It would be proper, of course, to examine the record from each farm for significant differences between the varieties, for even if these were not concordant they might indicate a greater aptitude of some varieties compared with others to the soil conditions of a particular site. Even in the absence of significant differences on individual farms, the results of the different experiments might be sufficiently concordant to give a significant comparison in the analysis of the entire experiment between varieties and error. This might not, however, be the most appropriate comparison to make, for since the varieties might react differently to different types of soil, it is not improbable that the mean square corresponding to the 36 degrees of freedom VP is greater than the mean square due to error. If the precision of the individual experiments were high, the difference between the aggregate yields of two varieties might be significant compared with error, although one was the better at only six places, while the other was better at the remaining four. In fact, if our concern is to ascertain not merely the best variety on the aggregate of the ten fields actually used, but to ascertain which is the best over the whole area deemed suitable for this type of crop, within the region from which the sites of the experiment have been selected, the comparison between varieties V and interaction of varieties and places VP will be the more appropriate. For, if the ten sites have been chosen at random from this area, a significant difference in this comparison would indicate, at the level of significance used, varietal differences applicable to the whole area. The precision of this comparison may not be greatly increased by higher precision in the individual experiments, especially if the mean square corresponding to VP is considerably greater than that ascribable to experimental error. To increase its precision we may rather require an increase in the number of sites used, or in other words, if the area sampled is considerably heterogeneous with respect to varietal response, it may be necessary to sample it more thoroughly. The hypothetical population with which we are principally concerned will then be the population of possible sites available for growing the crop under consideration, rather than the population of possible yields of plots within a given site. The test employed is, in fact, equivalent to considering, from each farm, only the aggregate yield of each variety, and the estimation of error within each individual Latin square is of value, apart from the local information supplied, only in providing assurance that the experimentation has been carried out with an exactitude sufficient to guarantee the adequacy of the comparisons between different places.

Cases in which it is one of the higher order interactions, rather than error proper, that should appropriately be used as a basis for tests of significance, are relatively numerous. The data of Table 7A (p. 66) are of this kind. Agricultural experiments, whether with manures, implements of cultivation or varieties of crop plants, are much affected by the weather. If a treatment effect is significant, compared with error in any one year, the experiment will have indicated what treatments have in that year proved most advantageous. But, if independent experiments over a series of years show a significant difference between treatments on the one hand and the interaction between treatments and years on the other, the experiment has shown what treatments are the most successful in an aggregate of seasons, of which those experienced may be taken as a random sample. There seems, in fact, in no part of the world to be any such similarity between successive seasons as would make the experience of a sequence of trials unreliable for future application in the absence of genuine secular changes of the climate.

The same principle is of wide application in economic and sociological enquiries, where, in comparisons of rates of death, morbidity, births, prices and so on, the effective unit is far more often a district, or a town, than an individual. The supposition that rates, based on the registration of individuals, possess the precision which would be appropriate if all the individuals concerned could be regarded as independent in their sociological reactions, is clearly inappropriate when we are interested in the effects on these reactions of economic or legislative causes, or other agencies derived from social organisation, liable to affect large numbers of individuals in a similar manner. The effective samples available for administrative decisions, even though based ultimately on millions of individual persons, are often much smaller than those available in biological experimentation, and for this reason require, even more than the latter, the accurate methods of analysis by which small samples may be interpreted.

REFERENCES AND OTHER READING

R. A. FISHER (1933). The concepts of inverse and fiducial probability referring to unknown parameters. Proceedings of the Royal Society, A, cxxxix., 343-348.

R. A. FISHER (1933). Two new properties of mathematical likelihood. Proceedings of the Royal Society, A, cxliv., 285-307.

R. A. FISHER (1933). The contributions of Rothamsted to the development of statistics. Rothamsted Experimental Station Report.

R. A. FISHER (1934). Probability, likelihood and quantity of information in the logic of uncertain inference. Proceedings of the Royal Society, A, cxlvi., 1-8.

E. J. MASKELL (1930). Field experiments. Journal of Tropical Agriculture, vii., 101-104, 125-131.

XI

THE MEASUREMENT OF AMOUNT OF INFORMATION IN GENERAL

66. Estimation in General

THE situations we shall now examine are of a more general character than those considered in the classical theory of errors, which have been dealt with in previous chapters. It has been seen in the last chapter that we may be interested to interpret the data as arising, subject to errors of unknown magnitude, but distributed normally, from one or more unknown quantities, *parameters*, of which we are interested to form *estimates*, of known precision, and to make this precision as great as possible. In the most general situation of this kind, all the different kinds of individual events which it is possible to observe are regarded as occurring with frequencies functionally dependent in any way on one or more of such unknown parameters. This is the general situation considered in the Theory of Estimation. From the purely statistical standpoint, they present the problem of how best the observations can be combined, in order to afford the most precise estimates possible of the unknowns. The mathematical principles of this process of combination are now satisfactorily understood, and have been illustrated in detail in the ninth chapter of the author's book, *Statistical Methods for Research Workers*. From the point of view of the practical design of experiments, or of observational programmes, we shall here be concerned only indirectly with the technique of the calculation of efficient estimates,

O

and can turn attention at once to the problem of assessing, in any particular case which arises, the quantity of information which the data supply, and which we may assume will be efficiently utilised.

The reason for this standpoint, so contrary to that traditional among statisticians, deserves some explanation. During the period in which highly inefficient methods of estimation were commonly employed, and, indeed, strongly advocated by the most influential authorities, it was natural that a great deal of ingenuity should be devoted, in each type of problem as it arose, to the invention of methods of estimation, with the idea always latent, though seldom clearly expressed, of making these as accurate as possible. The attainment of a result of high accuracy was, in fact, evidence not only of the intrinsic value of the data examined, but also to some extent of the skill with which it had been treated. The extent to which this was so was the greater the more inefficient were the methods ordinarily recommended ; but, clearly, in any subject in which the statistical methods ordinarily employed leave little to be desired, the precision of the result obtained will depend almost entirely on the value of the data on which it is based, and it is useless to commend the statistician, if this is great, or to reproach him if it is small. At the present time any novice in the theory of estimation should be able to set out the calculations necessary for making estimates, almost, if not quite, as good as they can possibly be. Any improvement which can be made by further refinements of computational technique are, in ordinary cases, and setting gross incompetence aside, exceedingly small compared to the improvements which may be effected in the observational data.

The amount of information to be expected in respect

of any unknown parameters, from a given number of observations of independent objects or events, the frequencies of which depend on that parameter, may be obtained by a simple application of the differential calculus. It may be worth while to consider a few easy examples in detail, in order to obtain a clear grasp of the process generally involved.

67. Frequencies of Two Alternatives

Let us suppose that only two kinds of objects or events are to be distinguished, and that we are concerned to estimate the frequency, p, with which one of them occurs as a fraction of all occurrences ; or, what comes to the same thing, the complementary frequency, q $(= 1 - p)$, with which the alternative event occurs. We might, for example, be estimating the proportion of males in the aggregate of live births, or the proportion of sterile samples drawn from a bulk in which an unknown number of organisms are distributed, or the proportion of experimental animals which die under well-defined experimental conditions. The experimental or observational record will then give us the numbers of the two kinds of observations made, a of one kind and b of another, out of a total number of n cases examined. We wish to know how much information the examination of n cases may be expected to provide, concerning the values of p and q, which are to be estimated from the data.

A general procedure, which may be easily applied to many cases, is to set down the frequencies to be expected in each of the distinguishable classes in terms of the unknown parameter. For each class we then find the differential coefficient, with respect to p, of this expectation. The squares of these, divided by the corresponding expectations, and added together, supply the amount of information to be anticipated from the observational record. That such a calculation will give a quantity of the kind we want, may be perceived at once by considering that the differential coefficients of the expectations, with respect to p, measure the rates at which these expectations will commence to be altered if p is gradually varied ; and the greater these rates are, whether the expectations are increased or diminished as p is increased, or in other words, whether the differential coefficients are positive or negative, the more sensitively will the expectations respond to variations of p. Consequently, it might have been anticipated that the value of the observational record for our purpose would be simply related to the squares of these differential coefficients.

We may now set out the process of calculation for the simple case of the estimation of the frequency of one of two classes.

TABLE 36

Observed Frequency. (x)	Expected Frequency. (m)	Differential Coefficient. dm/dp	$\frac{1}{m}\left(\frac{dm}{dp}\right)^2$
a	pn	n	n/p
b	qn	$-n$	n/q
n	n	0	n/pq

The frequencies expected are found by multiplying the number of observations, n, by the theoretical frequency, p, which is the object of estimation, and by its complementary frequency, q. The differential coefficients of these expectations with respect to p are simply n and $-n$. The sum of these is zero, as must be the case whenever, as is usual, the number of observations made is independent of the parameter to be estimated. It is obviously, therefore, not the total of the differential coefficients which measures the value of the data, but effectively the extent to which these differ in the different distinguishable classes, as measured by their squares appropriately weighted, as shown in the last column.

The total amount of information is found to be

$$I = \frac{n}{pq},$$

and we may now note the well-known fact that, if our sample of observations were indefinitely increased, the estimate of p, obtained from the data, tends in the limit to be distributed normally about the true value with variance $\frac{pq}{n}$. The general method here given of measuring quantity of information thus agrees with the concept, which has been formed of this quantity in previous chapters, where we were concerned only with normally distributed errors.

68. Functional Relationships among Parameters

It is often true that the frequency of a particular event among different events of a like kind is itself an object of enquiry, as is the case, for example, with the sex-ratio of births. More often the frequency is itself only of value because it is believed to be functionally related to some other quantity of more direct importance. The frequency, p, of sterile samples from a vessel containing an unknown density of organisms is related to the average number, m, of organisms in the sampling unit, by the relation,

$$p = e^{-m},$$
$$m = -\log p,$$

where the logarithm is taken from a table prepared on the natural or Napierian system.

If now the object of making a count discriminating only the two types of sample, viz., sterile samples which contain no organism, and fertile samples which contain at least one, is to make an estimate of the density in the material sampled, or in the material from which the dilution sampled was prepared, we shall be interested, not directly in the amount of information about p, but rather in the amount of information about m, which the sample provides. Since m and p are functionally related, this can be obtained by using the relationship directly, from the amount of information about p.

If in the table set out above, showing the calculation of the amount of information respecting p supplied by n observations, we had differentiated with respect to m instead of in respect to p, the process would have led to the amount of information with respect to m. The component terms of this calculation would each have differed from those we obtained only in containing, as an additional factor, the square of the differential coefficient of p with respect to m. In general, if I_m stands for the amount of information with respect to m, and I_p for the amount of information with respect to p, we have the transformation formula

$$I_m = \left(\frac{dp}{dm}\right)^2 I_p.$$

In the present case

$$p = e^{-m}$$

whence

$$\frac{dp}{dm} = -e^{-m} = -p.$$

And since

$$I_p = \frac{n}{pq}$$

it follows that

$$I_m = \frac{np}{q} = \frac{n}{e^m - 1}.$$

As in the case of p, if the number of samples examined is increased, our estimates of m derived from a given number of samples tend to be normally distributed about the true value, and the variance of this limiting distribution is given by the reciprocal of the amount of information,

$$V(m) = \frac{q}{pn} = \frac{e^m - 1}{n}.$$

The errors of estimation are least when m is near to zero, and increase rapidly if m is made large. This, however, does not mean that the determination will be most accurately carried out with very high dilutions, or with very small sampling units, by which means m may be made as small as we please ; for it must be remembered that if we reduce the sampling errors of m by making m smaller, we will not necessarily diminish the relative magnitude of these errors when compared with m. To minimise the relative magnitude of the sampling errors, we need to consider the variance of m divided by m^2 or, in fact the variance of $\log_e m$; thus

$$V(\log m) = \frac{1}{m^2} V(m) = \frac{1}{n} \frac{e^m - 1}{m^2}.$$

This quantity tends to infinite values when m is made either very small or very large. This expression for the limiting value of the relative variance in large samples, corresponds with the amount of information supplied by an experiment, however small, relative to $\log m$; for by the general transformation we find

$$I(\log m) = m^2 I_m ;$$

whence it appears equally that the amount of information supplied by the experiment relative to $\log m$ is given by the expression

$$I = n \frac{m^2}{e^m - 1}.$$

This quantity vanishes as m tends to zero or infinity, but is finite at all intermediate values ; and the relative precision of our estimate of the number of organisms will be greatest if the dilution or the sampling unit were adjusted, so as to maximise this quantity.

Fig. 3 shows the quantity of information, for all values of m, for which this quantity is not very small.

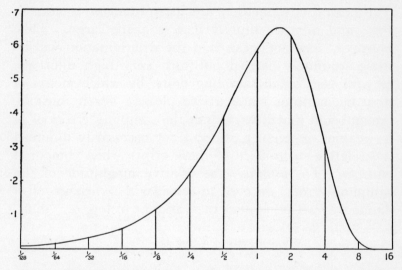

FIG. 3.—Quantity of information as to the density of organisms in a medium according to the average number m of organisms per sample.

The horizontal scale is logarithmic, so that values of m indicated at equal intervals are in geometric progression. It is evident from the figure that the most useful values are between about 1·1 and 2·2. The absolute maximum of information is given when m is about 1·6, or, more precisely, a number $\hat{m}$ with rather remarkable properties, such that

$$1 - e^{-\hat{m}} = \tfrac{1}{2}\hat{m} \; ;$$

since

$$p = e^{-\hat{m}}$$

it follows that the ratio of $\hat{p}$ to $\hat{q}$ is the same as the ratio of $(2-\hat{m})$ to $\hat{m}$. Numerically, it appears that

$$\hat{m} = 1{\cdot}593{,}624{,}26$$
$$1-e^{-\hat{m}} = {\cdot}796{,}812{,}13 = \tfrac{1}{2}\hat{m} = \hat{q}.$$
$$2-\hat{m} = {\cdot}406{,}375{,}74$$
$$e^{-\hat{m}} = {\cdot}203{,}187{,}87 = 1-\tfrac{1}{2}\hat{m} = \hat{p}.$$

The ideal proportion of sterile samples for estimating by this method the density of the organisms is, therefore, just over 20 per cent. Any proportion between 10 per cent. and 33 per cent. sterile will, however, supply nearly as much information, and the aim in adjusting the sampling process should be to obtain a percentage of sterile samples between these limits. The maximal amount of information per sample is

$$\hat{i} = {\cdot}647{,}610{,}24 = \hat{m}(2-\hat{m}) = 4\hat{p}\hat{q}.$$

To find the minimal number of samples needed to estimate m with any given precision, we may now equate $n\hat{i}$ to the invariance of $\log m$ required. Thus if we required to reduce the standard error of m to about 10 per cent. of its value, we might put the standard error of $\log m$ equal to $0{\cdot}1$; the variance of $\log m$ would then be $0{\cdot}01$ and its invariance would be 100. We should then have

$$n\hat{i} = 100,$$
or
$$n = 154{\cdot}4.$$

Even in the most favourable circumstances, therefore, it would need 155 samples to reduce the standard error below 10 per cent. of the estimated density. Since, owing to our ignorance of the true density, the dilution cannot be adjusted exactly so as to give the ideal proportion of sterile samples, it would usually be wise to divide the amount of information required by a smaller divisor than the maximal value ·6477, *e.g.* by ·6, which would raise our estimated requirement to 167 samples. The whole calculation shows that the method of estimating the density of organisms by discriminating only their presence, or absence, in samples is of low precision, compared with methods in which individuals or colonies may be counted.

In many types of research a series of dilutions is employed, giving densities falling off in geometric progression, with a constant factor most commonly of 2 or 10. The amounts of information supplied by each of these is represented in the diagram (Fig. 3) by the heights of a series of equally spaced ordinates. If the series is extended so as to cover all densities which supply an appreciable amount of information, the sum of the ordinates for two-fold dilution is nearly constant in value and has an average value

$$\frac{\pi^2}{6 \log_e 2} = 2 \cdot 373,138.$$

This is, therefore, the amount of information supplied by a single sample at each dilution, and this may be used to calculate the precision to be expected, using any number of samples at each dilution, or to calculate the number of samples required to attain any stipulated level of precision. For four-fold dilutions the average amount of information supplied is, of course, a half, and for eight-fold dilutions one-third of the number found above. For ten-fold dilutions it is about three-tenths, but for the higher dilution ratios the sum of the ordinates shows a rapidly increasing variation, with the consequence that the amount of information actually obtained becomes less reliable the larger the dilution-ratio employed.

69. The Frequency Ratio in Biological Assay

Use is often made of a frequency ratio between two distinguishable classes, to supply a measure of an underlying variate, as when the toxic content of a drug is inferred from the mortality of experimental animals receiving a known dosage, or from the dosage required to cause a given mortality. The underlying theory is illustrated in Fig. 4. The curve represents a normal distribution with unit standard deviation, divided by

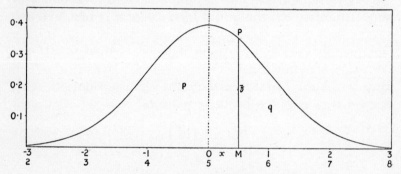

FIG. 4.—Normal distribution curve to illustrate the interpretation of percentage mortality as a probit value.

the ordinate P M into two portions. The area to the left of the ordinate represents the proportion, p, which die under the treatment, the area to the right the proportion, q, which survive. The height of the ordinate is represented by z, and its distance from the central axis of the curve by x, taken positive to the right of the axis. As x increases from $-\infty$ to ∞, the proportion dying increases from 0 to 1. Knowing any of the three quantities x, p or z, the other two can be obtained from available tables. An experimental determination of the fraction, p, will therefore supply a corresponding determination of the deviation, x, and this is found, in a large number of cases, to increase or decrease proportionally with the logarithm of the toxic content of the dose. If, therefore, the relationship between dosage and mortality has been established for a standard preparation, the toxicity of any material under test may be gauged by observing the mortality which supervenes on a known dosage of the material to be tested. Moreover, so long as a linear relation holds between the toxic content measured logarithmically and the deviation, x, the precision of the assay will be proportional to the precision with which x is estimated.

As is seen from the figure, if x is increased by a small quantity dx, the initial increase of p is $z\,dx$. Hence

$$\frac{dp}{dx} = z.$$

But we know that the amount of information with respect to x is given by the equation

$$I_x = I_p \left(\frac{dp}{dx}\right)^2$$
$$= \frac{nz^2}{pq},$$

where n is the number of animals employed. Although $\frac{1}{pq}$ is least when p equals q, or at 50 per cent. mortality, the quantity of information, $\frac{nz^2}{pq}$, is greatest at this point. Hence for a single test, the highest precision is obtained for a given number of animals by adjusting the dosage approximately to the 50 per cent. death point. The quantity

$$I = \frac{nz^2}{pq}$$

is used further as the weight to be assigned to the estimated value of x when a number of tests at different dosages are to be combined. The quantity $5+x$, known as the " probit value," is used as a practical measure of mortality, and Dr C. I. Bliss has given tables of the weighting factor, and other relationships needed for the more complex problems which arise in toxicological research. Fig. 5 shows the amount of information respecting the probit value supplied by each animal observed, for different percentage mortalities. It will

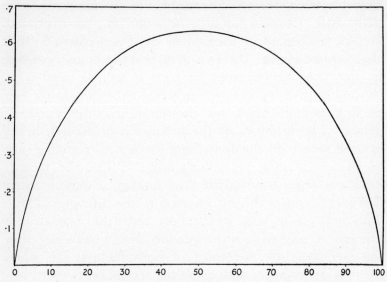

FIG. 5.—The amount of information as to the probit in terms of the percentage mortality.

be seen that when the mortality is between one-third and two-thirds, the information gained falls little short of the highest possible.

Tables and illustrations of their use are given in *Statistical Tables*.

70. Linkage Values inferred from Frequency Ratios

When an organism receives from its two parents corresponding genes of different kinds, it generally hands on one kind to half its offspring and the other kind to the remainder. The numbers of the two kinds of offspring observed may, however, differ, either by chance or owing to the unequal viability of these two kinds. The parent is said to be heterozygous for the Mendelian factor in question. If the parent is heterozygous for two different factors, which are not linked in inheritance, he may make contributions of four different kinds to the germinal constitution of the offspring, and these will occur in equal numbers. If, however, the factors are linked, or carried in the germ-plasm by the same chromosome, the two gene-combinations received by the heterozygote from his parents will be handed on to the offspring more frequently than the remaining two combinations formed by interchanging the pairs of genes. The intensity of the linkage is measured, in an inverse sense, by the frequency among all the offspring of those receiving recombinations. When the recombination frequency is small, the linkage is close ; when it is large, approaching 50 per cent., the linkage is loose. The type of mating which best tests the intensity of linkage is one with an organism distinguishable from the heterozygote in respect of both factors, *i.e.* when there is dominance, with a double recessive.

If there is no difference in mortality among the four distinguishable types of offspring, up to the time at which they can be recorded, any such mating will determine the linkage value, with precision limited only by the number of offspring. Thus, if a fraction, p, of recombinations is estimated from a count of n offspring, the amount of information available as to the value of p is

$$I = \frac{n}{pq}.$$

If, however, the two types counted as recombinations have an average viability different from that of the two types of parental combinations, the linkage value so estimated will be distorted by the differential mortality. It is possible to overcome this difficulty by making up heterozygotes of the two kinds possible, so that the recombinations from one set of matings are genetically similar to the parental combinations from the other. Thus, if in one set the apparent recombination value has been raised by differential viability, it will have been lowered in the other set. If, therefore, we have a record of two such sets of matings as shown in the following table

	Recombination.	Parental Combination.	Total.
1st set . . .	a_1	b_1	n_1
2nd set . . .	a_2	b_2	n_2

we may argue that the ratio a_1/b_1 has been raised (or lowered) in the first set in the same proportion as the ratio a_2/b_2 has been lowered (or raised) in the second. Hence, if we take the geometric mean of these two ratios, and use, as our equation of estimation,

$$\frac{p}{q} = \sqrt{\frac{a_1 a_2}{b_1 b_2}},$$

we shall obtain an estimate unbiased by differential mortality, in so far as it is caused by the factors studied.

To determine the precision of such an estimate, we may consider first the precision with which the quantity

$$\log \frac{p}{q} = \log p - \log q$$

is derived from a simple frequency ratio $a : b$; since

$$\frac{d}{dp} \log \frac{p}{q} = \frac{1}{p} + \frac{1}{q} = \frac{1}{pq},$$

it follows that

$$\mathrm{I}_{\log p/q} = p^2 q^2 \mathrm{I}_p = p^2 q^2 \frac{n}{pq} = npq;$$

and since, as our estimate, we shall put

$$p = \frac{a}{n}, \ q = \frac{b}{n},$$

the amount of information may be written,

$$I = \frac{ab}{n} \ ;$$

or, in large samples, the sampling variance of $\log \frac{p}{q}$ is

$$\frac{a+b}{ab} = \frac{1}{a} + \frac{1}{b}.$$

Now, in estimating $\log \frac{p}{q}$ from the geometric mean of two observed ratios, we are taking half the sum of two estimates of $\log \frac{p}{q}$, and the sampling variance will therefore be one-quarter of the sum of the four reciprocals.

Hence,

$$V = \frac{1}{4}\left(\frac{1}{a_1} + \frac{1}{b_1} + \frac{1}{a_2} + \frac{1}{b_2} \right).$$

$$I = \frac{4}{\dfrac{1}{a_1} + \dfrac{1}{b_1} + \dfrac{1}{a_2} + \dfrac{1}{b_2}} = h,$$

where h is the harmonic mean of the four frequencies observed.

The information respecting the recombination fraction, p, estimated in this way, may be calculated, as before, from that respecting $\log \frac{p}{q}$, and is evidently

$$I_p = h/p^2 q^2.$$

We may now ask in what proportions the two types of mating should be used, in order to secure the greatest precision for a given number of organisms bred and examined.

If p_1, q_1 stand for the proportions observed from

matings of the first kind, and p_2, q_2 from matings of the second kind, the amount of information has been shown to be inversely proportional to

or to
$$\frac{1}{n_1 p_1} + \frac{1}{n_1 q_1} + \frac{1}{n_2 p_2} + \frac{1}{n_2 q_2},$$

$$\frac{1}{n_1 p_1 q_1} + \frac{1}{n_2 p_2 q_2}.$$

We wish to make this quantity as small as possible, consistently with a fixed total of organisms observed, $n_1 + n_2$. If the numbers are such as to make this quantity a minimum, it will be unaltered by a small decrement in the number n_1, accompanied by a corresponding small increment in the number n_2. But if n_1 is diminished and n_2 increased by a small change dn, the quantity above is increased by

$$\frac{dn}{n_1^2 p_1 q_1} - \frac{dn}{n_2^2 p_2 q_2}.$$

Hence for the most satisfactory proportion,

$$n_1^2 p_1 q_1 = n_2^2 p_2 q_2.$$

We should then endeavour to adjust our observational numbers so that

$$a_1 b_1 = a_2 b_2 ;$$

in other words, the product of the observed frequencies from one set of matings should be approximately equal to the product from the other set.

By reversing the manner in which the frequencies are combined, the data may be used to determine differential viability, in the same way as they are used to estimate the recombination frequency. The consequence is that the same proportionate numbers from the two types of mating, which are ideal for the estimation of linkage, are also ideal for the estimation of differential viability.

P

71. Linkage Values inferred from the Progeny of Self-fertilised or Intercrossed Heterozygotes

With many plants it is easier to ensure self-fertilisation than to execute controlled crossings, consequently much of the information available as to linkage in plants is derived from the families of self-fertilised heterozygotes. With animals also such data are obtained in the course of combining two recessives not yet available in combination. Methods of estimating the intensity of linkage have been examined in Chapter IX. of the author's *Statistical Methods*, and analogous but more complex cases have been discussed by J. B. Hutchinson and F. R. Immer. We are here only concerned with the evaluation, in such problems, of the quantity of information as to the linkage value postulated, which the data make available. If there is reason to suspect differential viability, there is no satisfactory substitute for back-crossing, so we shall discuss only the case in which this complication is absent.

The frequencies of the four distinguishable types to be expected may best be inferred from that of the double recessives, for this is only produced when both of the uniting gametes lack both dominant genes. When the two dominant genes have been received by the parents from different grandparents (repulsion), the proportion of such doubly recessive gametes will be $\frac{1}{2} p$, where p is the recombination fraction. The probability that both the uniting gametes are of this kind is therefore $\frac{1}{4} p^2$, or $\frac{1}{4} p p'$ if the recombination fractions should be different in male and female gametogenesis, and are represented by p and p'. We may, therefore, represent this fraction by $\frac{1}{4} \theta$, noting that for repulsion $\sqrt{\theta}$ will be the recombination fraction, or at least the geometric mean of the two recombination fractions, if there are two different values. The frequencies, in any case, are expressible in terms of θ. Consequently, it is only of this quantity that the data provide information. The data provide no means of detecting any difference that may exist between p and p', and we shall from this point use the symbol χ merely as an equivalent to $\sqrt{\theta}$. In the case of coupling, on the other hand, the doubly recessive gametes will be of the parental combination, and the recombination fraction will be $1-\chi$.

From the expected proportion of double recessives the proportions of the other classes may be easily inferred from the fact that each recessive separately must appear in one-quarter of the offspring, irrespective of linkage. The two singly recessive genotypes have, therefore, each a proportional expectation of $\frac{1}{4}(1-\theta)$, leaving $\frac{1}{4}(2+\theta)$ for the last, or doubly dominant type.

Having evaluated the expectations, we may now, as before, calculate directly the amount of information which a record of n offspring will supply as to the value of θ. The table below shows this calculation.

TABLE 37

Offspring expected. (m).	$dm/d\theta$.	$\frac{1}{m}\left(\dfrac{dm}{d\theta}\right)^2$.	Total.
$\dfrac{n}{4}\theta$	$\dfrac{n}{4}$	$n/4\theta$	
$\dfrac{n}{4}(1-\theta)$	$-\dfrac{n}{4}$	$n/4(1-\theta)$	$\dfrac{2n(1+2\theta)}{4\theta(1-\theta)(2+\theta)}$
$\dfrac{n}{4}(1-\theta)$	$-\dfrac{n}{4}$	$n/4(1-\theta)$	
$\dfrac{n}{4}(2+\theta)$	$\dfrac{n}{4}$	$n/4(2+\theta)$	

from which it appears that

$$I_\theta = \frac{n(1+2\theta)}{2\theta(1-\theta)(2+\theta)}$$

for all values of θ. It will be noted that the second and third classes of offspring, the expectations of which are the same functions of θ, might have been treated together without altering the result. In fact, we are only concerned with the total number in these two classes, and not with the parts of which this total is composed, in estimating the value of θ. The fact that these two classes are usually distinguishable adds nothing to our information. The same applies wherever distinguishable classes have proportional frequencies.

Knowing the information available respecting θ, we can now obtain the quantity of information respecting χ. For, since

$$\theta = \chi^2,$$
$$d\theta/d\chi = 2\chi,$$

and

$$\left(\frac{d\theta}{d\chi}\right)^2 = 4\chi^2 = 4\theta.$$

Hence

$$i_\chi = 4\theta\, i_\theta = \frac{2(1+2\theta)}{(1-\theta)(2+\theta)}.$$

This quantity rises steadily from the value unity when $\theta = 0$, the closest possible linkage in repulsion, through 16/9 when $\theta = \frac{1}{4}$, linkage being absent, to an infinite value when $\theta = 1$, the limit of close linkage in coupling. When linkage is at all close, therefore, interbreeding of heterozygotes in coupling is immensely more informative, for the same number of offspring, than the interbreeding of heterozygotes in repulsion. Roughly speaking, with 10 per cent. recombination, coupling matings are worth about ten times as much as repulsion matings; and if the recombination fraction is as small as 5 per cent., they are worth about twenty times as much.

Lack of recognition of this great contrast between the amounts of information supplied by these two types of progenies has led, on several occasions in the genetical literature, to curious misinterpretations of the genetical results. Indeed, it greatly delayed the discovery of the phenomenon of linkage itself, for English geneticists, discussing undoubted cases of linkage in plants, while observing the occurrence of recombination among the coupling progenies, failed to recognise its occurrence in the progenies from heterozygotes in repulsion, and were led to believe that these two different aspects of the same problem followed different laws. The discovery of linkage was thus delayed until animal geneticists, working with a biparental organism, *Drosophila*, in which back-crossing is as convenient as the interbreeding of heterozygotes, demonstrated that the recombination fraction was the same, irrespective of whether the two dominant genes entered the cross from the same or from different parents. Had the plant geneticists been aware that a progeny of 200 offspring in repulsion might be equivalent, in evidential value, to some 25 offspring in coupling, they would, perhaps, have grown sufficiently numerous repulsion progenies to have demonstrated the identity of the two phenomena, which had attracted their attention.

A number of further inferences of practical interest follow from the evaluation of the amount of information to be derived from progenies by self-fertilisation, which the reader may usefully verify for himself.

(1) With close linkage, progenies obtained by self-fertilising heterozygotes in coupling are of nearly equivalent value with back-cross progenies. Thus the advantage of back-crossing when it is possible, lies, in cases of close linkage, principally in the opportunity it affords of eliminating, and of evaluating, differential viability, and of detecting any difference there may be in the recombination fraction in male and female gametogenesis.

(2) When no double recessives are available, the only double heterozygotes that can be formed are in repulsion. Self-fertilising or interbreeding these supplies very little information when the linkage is close. When, however, on growing such a progeny, this situation is found to have occurred, the plant geneticist has usually the choice of two alternative methods of adding to his information in the next generation. (*a*) He may repeat his previous procedure on a large scale, and (*b*) he may grow selfed progenies from the last generation, and so ascertain which are homozygous and which heterozygous, and among the double heterozygotes, which are in coupling and which in repulsion. Supposing the land and labour required to grow each such family to be equivalent to that of growing 25 self-fertilised plants of the kind first obtained, procedure (*b*) will be the more profitable when linkage is very close, and less profitable when it is looser. It is an instructive problem to ascertain at what linkage value the two methods are equally advantageous. In considering this problem it should be noted that in procedure (*b*) the geneticist may choose to form families from the singly recessive plants, or from the double dominants, or from both, but has clearly nothing to learn from the doubly recessive plants. The value of the second season's work will lie, not in the total information gained by a complete classification, but only in information additional to what has been gained by the first season's work. In the second season, however, there will be some further information, from the progenies of 25 plants each from those self-fertilised plants which happen to be double heterozygotes, and of these a certain proportion must be expected to be in coupling.

72. Information as to Linkage derived from Human Families

The greatest obstacle to the study of linkage in man is that it is seldom possible to test or examine for known factors so many as three generations of a family showing any hereditary peculiarity. Consequently, when double heterozygotes are found among parents, it is not known, supposing there is linkage, whether they are in coupling or repulsion. Apart from recent race mixture, however, and other causes of disturbance, these two phases may be expected to occur in equal numbers and, indeed, this fact, when true, can be verified from the family records of only two generations. The possibility of obtaining from such records indications of linkage was first proposed by Bernstein by the use of methods, however, which do not in general utilise the whole of the information in the record. The problem has since been more fully discussed by Haldane and others. We shall here only illustrate the general method of assessing the amount of information obtainable by a classification of the different kinds of families in the record.

Many rare anomalies are transmitted from generation to generation by persons heterozygous for the mutants responsible. If these and their spouses and children are examined for some known factor, such as the capacity for tasting phenylthiocarbamide, a certain number will be heterozygous tasters. Since homozygous tasters cannot be discriminated from heterozygotes, this will only be known if the affected parent is a taster, and if at least one of the children is a non-taster. Only such families can, therefore, be included in the record. Apart from the classification of the children, such families are of two kinds : (a) in which the normal parent is a non-taster, for which Bernstein's method is satisfactory; and (*b*) in which the normal parent is a heterozygous taster, for which it is less successful, and which we may take as an example.

The families of two in such a record are of seven possible kinds, which are shown in Table 38 below, where distinguishable individuals are denoted as follows : the affected A, normals a, tasters T, non-tasters t. The first six kinds of family are arranged in the table in

TABLE 38

Types of Family.	Frequency expected.		m.	$dm/d\xi$.	m.	$\frac{1}{m}\left(\frac{dm}{d\xi}\right)^2$.
AT At aT at	Coupling.	Repulsion.			$\xi=\frac{1}{4}$	$\xi=\frac{1}{4}$
0 0 0 2 0 2 0 0	χ^2 $(1-\chi)^2$	$(1-\chi)^2$ χ^2	$\Big\}\ 1-2\xi$	-2	$\frac{1}{2}$	8
1 0 0 1 0 1 1 0	$2\chi(1+\chi)$ $2(1-\chi)(2-\chi)$	$2(1-\chi)(2-\chi)$ $2\chi(1+\chi)$	$\Big\}\ 4(1-\xi)$	-4	3	16/3
0 0 1 1 1 1 0 0	$2\chi(2-\chi)$ $2(1-\chi^2)$	$2(1-\chi^2)$ $2\chi(2-\chi)$	$\Big\}\ 2(1+2\xi)$	$+4$	3	16/3
0 1 0 1	$2\chi(1-\chi)$	$2\chi(1-\chi)$	2ξ	$+2$	$\frac{1}{2}$	8
			7	0	7	80/3

pairs, each member of which has the same frequency for heterozygotes in coupling as the other has for repulsion. The combined frequency of these two kinds of family is thus independent of the relative frequency of these two kinds of heterozygotes, while the equality of frequency of members of the same pair will serve to confirm the view that the two types of heterozygote are equally frequent, or, if this were not so, to estimate their relative frequency. We shall here be concerned only with the combined frequency of these pairs. This combined frequency, being a symmetrical function of the recombination fraction, χ, and its complement $1-\chi$, may be simply expressed in terms of the product,

$$\xi = \chi(1-\chi).$$

The expected frequencies are shown in the table for a total of seven suitable families observed.

In order to assess the efficacy of the classification in detecting linkage, we need to know the amount of information which it provides in the limit for loose linkage, when $\chi = \frac{1}{2}$, and $\xi = \frac{1}{4}$. After calculating, therefore, the values of $dm/d\xi$ for the four types of family to be distinguished, the frequencies are rewritten for the particular value $\xi = \frac{1}{4}$, and the amount of information calculated for this value in the last column. It is easily seen that the total amount of information is 80/3 for seven families, or the information per family is

$$i = 80/21.$$

The loss of information in Bernstein's method arises from the fact that he draws no distinction between the types of family in the first and second pairs, or between the third pair and the last type of family. If we were to throw these together, so distinguishing only two groups of families, and relying on the relative frequencies of these two groups only for the detection of linkage, we should have the table set out below.

TABLE 39

	m.	$dm/d\xi$.	m. $\xi=\frac{1}{4}$	$\dfrac{1}{m}\left(\dfrac{dm}{d\xi}\right)^2$. $\xi=\frac{1}{4}$
First group	$5-6\xi$	-6	$3\frac{1}{2}$	$72/7$
Second group . . .	$2+6\xi$	$+6$	$3\frac{1}{2}$	$72/7$
Totals . .	7	0	7	$144/7$

The amount of information available from seven families, using Bernstein's classification, is therefore only 144/7, in place of 80/3 available when the families are fully classified. The fraction of the information utilised by Bernstein's method is the ratio of these two quantities, or 27/35. This ratio is termed the efficiency of the method. For larger families its value is found to be somewhat, but not much, lower, the limiting value for large families being 9/16. There is, however, no difficulty in utilising the whole of the information available in the record for families of any size, once the loss of information, and its cause, are recognised. The reader may find it instructive to examine in like manner the classification of families of three children.

73. The Information elicited by Different Methods of Estimation

The foregoing example illustrates the fact, of very general importance, that methods of estimation which proceed without reference to the possibility of evaluating the quantity of information actually contained in the data, are liable to be defective in the quantity that they utilise. When, as is usual, many methods of estimation are available, it becomes important to be able to distinguish which use less, which more, and which, if any, use all. Since the method of measuring information, which has been illustrated, is applicable to data of all kinds, it is only necessary, in order to ascertain how much information is utilised by any proposed method, to determine the sampling distribution of the estimates obtained by that method from quantities of data of the same value as those observed. It is often possible, though sometimes a matter of great mathematical difficulty, to obtain the exact sampling distribution of the estimate arrived at by any particular method, and in such cases the amount of information elicited by the estimate is that of a single observation drawn from this distribution, calculated exactly as in the cases illustrated above.

In many cases in which the exact distribution of an estimate derived from a finite body of data is unknown, it is easy to show that as the sample is increased in magnitude, the sampling distribution tends to the normal form with a calculable variance, V, inversely proportional to the size of the sample, so that

$$ V = \frac{v}{n}, $$

where v is calculable for any chosen method of estimation.

We shall now show, by a direct application of the general method of calculating the information to such a distribution of a proposed statistic, that the amount of information elicited by the statistic is $\frac{n}{v}$.

Since, in the limiting case considered, the distribution of the statistic becomes continuous and all observable values of it are distinguishable, instead of a summation over a number of classes, we shall be concerned with an integration over all the elementary ranges, dT, in which the statistic T may be found to lie. T, then, is known to be distributed about the true value θ of the parameter, whatever it may be, of which T is an estimate in a normal distribution with known variance, V. The probability that it will be found to lie in the infinitesimal range, dT, is therefore,

$$ df = \frac{1}{\sqrt{2\pi V}} e^{-\frac{(T-\theta)^2}{2V}} d\mathrm{T}. $$

Differentiating this with respect to θ, in order to ascertain how much information about θ the value of T, regarded now as a single observation, provides, we have

$$\frac{T-\theta}{V}\, df.$$

The square of this divided by df is now seen to be

$$\frac{(T-\theta)^2}{V^2} df,$$

and the integration of this over all values of T gives simply

$$\frac{V}{V^2} = \frac{1}{V},$$

since, as is well known, the average value of $(T-\theta)^2$ is equal to V, V being, in fact, the mean square deviation, or variance, of the normal distribution.

Consequently, we have found that the amount of information provided by an estimate, normally distributed with variance V, is equal to $1/V$, the *invariance* of that normal distribution. It is thus easy to test whether in the limit for large samples any proposed method of estimation tends to elicit the whole of the information supplied by the data, or a lesser amount. We have only to compare the quantity $1/V$ with I, the amount known to be available ; or, dividing both of these quantities by n, to compare $1/v$ with the amount of information, i, provided by each individual observation. The ratio of the amount elicited to the amount available is called the " efficiency " of the method of estimation under discussion, and it has been demonstrated, as the common sense of the method requires, that the efficiency can in no circumstances exceed unity.

74. The Information lost in the Estimation of Error

In the limit for large samples it is always possible to obtain estimates of 100 per cent. efficiency, but with small samples, when treated exactly, this is not found to be generally possible. In some simple cases, however, estimates may be made, which in themselves contain the whole of the information available for finite samples. These especially valuable and comprehensive estimates are called *sufficient* statistics, and the great simplicity of the problems, which fall under the head of the theory of errors, is due to the fact that with the normal distribution both of the quantities requiring estimation, the mean, and the variance, possess sufficient estimates. It is for this reason that in so much experimental work we need only be concerned with the precision of the total, or mean, of the values observed, and with the estimation of this precision from the sum of the squares of the residual deviations.

There is, however, one point in connection with experiments involving measurements, to which the theory of errors is applicable, which may be cleared up by the methods of this chapter.

When, as the result of an experiment, a value x has been assigned a sampling variance, s^2, validly and correctly estimated from n degrees of freedom, the position is not the same as if the variance were known with exactitude. Our estimate of the variance is itself subject to sampling error, and exact allowance for such error is made by using the true distribution of t, instead of the normal distribution, when testing the significance of the deviation of our observed value from any proposed hypothetical value. In view of this procedure, it must be considered to be inexact to state the amount of information supplied by the experiment respecting the true value of which x is an estimate, merely as $1/s^2$, as though our estimate were known to be normally distributed with this variance. We need, in fact, in considering the absolute precision of an experimental result, to take into account, not only the estimate s^2 derived from the data, but also the number of degrees of freedom upon which our estimate, s^2, was based.

Now the probability that the quantity t, defined by the relationship

$$x - \mu = st,$$

where x is the observed value and μ the hypothetical value of which it is an estimate, shall lie in any assigned range, dt, is given by the formula

$$df = \frac{\dfrac{n-1}{2}!}{\dfrac{n-2}{2}!\ \sqrt{\pi n}} \cdot \frac{dt}{\left(1 + \dfrac{t^2}{n}\right)^{\frac{1}{2}(n+1)}};$$

or in terms of x and μ, by

$$df = \frac{\dfrac{n-1}{2}!}{\dfrac{n-2}{2}!\ s\sqrt{\pi n}} \cdot \frac{dx}{\left\{1 + \dfrac{(x-\mu)^2}{ns^2}\right\}^{\frac{1}{2}(n+1)}}.$$

From this we can evaluate the amount of information supplied by an observed value, x, relative to the unknown parameter, μ, as we have done with the normal curve above, by differentiating with respect to μ. This gives

$$\frac{n+1}{n\,s^2} \cdot \frac{(x-\mu)df}{1 + \dfrac{(x-\mu)^2}{n\,s^2}};$$

squaring this, and dividing by df, we find

$$\frac{(n+1)^2}{n^2\,s^4} \cdot \frac{(x-\mu)^2 df}{\left\{1 + \dfrac{(x-\mu)^2}{ns^2}\right\}^2}.$$

When integrated over all possible values of the observable quantity, x, this amounts to

$$\frac{n+1}{(n+3)s^2}.$$

It appears that the true precision of our estimate is somewhat lower than it would have been, had the variance been known with exactitude to be s^2. In the extreme case, when $n = 1$, and the estimate is based on only 1 degree of freedom, the precision is halved. And in general, the true precision is less than it might be thought, if the uncertainty of our estimate of the variance were ignored, by the fraction $2/(n+3)$. It may thus be worth while to sacrifice, to some small extent, the aim of diminishing the value of s^2, if this diminution carries with it any undue reduction in the number of degrees of freedom, available for the estimation of error.

REFERENCES AND OTHER READING

C. I. BLISS (1935). The calculation of the dosage mortality curve. Annals of Applied Biology, xxii. 134-167.

C. I. BLISS (1935). The comparison of dosage mortality data. Annals of Applied Biology, xxii. 307-333.

R. A. FISHER (1922). On the mathematical foundations of theoretical statistics. The Philosophical Transactions of the Royal Society, A, ccxxii. 309-68.

R. A. FISHER (1925-48). Statistical Methods for Research Workers. Chapter IX.

R. A. FISHER and BHAI BALMUKAND (1928). The estimation of linkage from the offspring of selfed heterozygotes. Journal of Genetics, xx. 79-92.

R. A. FISHER (1934). The amount of information supplied by records of families as a function of the linkage in the population sampled. Annals of Eugenics, vi. 66-70.

240   REFERENCES AND OTHER READING

J. B. Hutchinson (1929). The application of the " Method of Maximum Likelihood " to the estimation of linkage. Genetics, xiv. 514-537.

F. R. Immer (1934). Calculating linkage intensities from F_3 data. Genetics, xix. 119-136.

R. A. Fisher and F. Yates (1938, 1943, 1948). Statistical Tables. Oliver and Boyd Ltd., Edinburgh.

R. A. Fisher (1943). The theory of confounding in factorial experiments in relation to the theory of groups. Annals of Eugenics, xi. 4, 341-353.

R. A. Fisher (1945). A system of confounding for factors with more than two alternations, giving completely orthogonal cubes and higher powers. Annals of Eugenics, xii. 4, 283-290.

INDEX

Amount of information, 182-185, 209-240

Analysis of covariance, 169-173

Analysis of variance, 50-56, 71-72, 98, 99, 112-144, 127, 136, 149, 170, 172, 196-204

Annual crops, 164

Arbitrary corrections, 166

Balmukand, 239

Barley, 65, 66, 140

Basis of inference, 99

Bayes, 5-7, 10

Bernstein, 231-234

Bias, 62, 63, 72

Biological assay, 219-221

Bliss, 221, 239

Boole, 4

Bose, 134

Boyle, xi

Cabinet Cyclopædia, 4

χ^2 test, 193-196

Chrystal, 4

Complete orthogonalisation, 133

Components of error, 143

Concomitant measurements, 161-181

Confounding, 107-134

Costing, 184

Cotton spinning, 86

Cyclic sets, 154

Cyclic substitution, 123

Darwin, 26, 31, 37, 39, 43, 47, 55, 186, 189, 196

De Morgan, 4, 6, 10

Digitalis, 27

Dilution method, 214-219

Drosophila, 229

Dummy comparisons, 315-137

Eden, 55, 67

Efficiency, 236

Ely, 88

Estimation, 209

Factorial design, 91-106

Fiducial probability, 182, 195

Galton, 27, 28, 30, 38, 39-40, 43

General hypothesis, 43-47

Good Easter, 179

Græco-Latin Square, 78-83, 157

Groups, 115

Haldane, 231

Hayes, 65, 67

Hutchinson, 226, 240

Immer, 65, 67, 226, 240

Induction, 3, 99

Interaction, 95-99, 105, 110 133, 204-209

Interpretation, 1, 12, 150-152

Invariance, 182, 236

Inverse probability, 6

Ipomœa, 27

Laplace, 4

Latin Square, 68-90, 119, 122, 123, 124, 127, 140, 176, 196, 203

Lavoisier, xi

Limnanthes, 27, 30

Linkage, 221-234

241

Maskell, 190, 208
Minnesota, 65
Missing values, 175-178

Nair, 134
Norton, 81, 90
Null hypothesis, 15-17, 182-208

Orthogonal sets, 124-127
Orthogonal squares, 78-81

Pairing, 31-35
Parameters, 209-213
Partial confounding, 127-160
Perennial crops, 164
Petunia, 27
Pigs, 169
Potatoes, 88
Powers, 65, 67
Precision, 21-25, 56-58, 182, 215-240
Price, 6
Probit, 219-231
Problem of distribution, 16
Psycho-physical experiment, 11

Quantity and quality, 137-139

Randomisation, 17-21, 40-43, 49-50,
    60-64, 68-70
Randomised blocks, 48-50
Ratio, fiducial limits of, 192-193
References, 10, 25, 47, 67 90, 106,
    134, 160, 181, 208, 239-240
Regression, 138, 169
Replication, 58-60, 88, 106

Reseda lutea, 27
Rothamsted, 88, 140, 152, 180, 181

Sanders, 181
Sex ratio, 211-213
Shape of blocks and plots, 64-65
Significance, 13, 33, 55, 73, 105, 113
    182
Skewness, 188
Spindles, 83
Statistical control, 161-181
Stewart, Lyle, 178
" Student," 33, 38, 47, 189-190
Subsidiary factors, 100
Sugar-beet, 177
Systematic designs, 62, 74-78

t test, 33-37, 43-47, 186, 189, 192
Tea, 11, 164
Tedin, 78, 90
Theory of errors, 26
Theory of estimation, 209
Tippett, 50, 67, 86

Venn, 4
Vik, 76, 78
Viola, 27

Wishart, 160

Yates, 46, 55, 67, 82, 90, 134

z test, 55, 56, 57, 73, 150, 196, 197,
    204
Zea, 27-30

PRINTED IN GREAT BRITAIN BY OLIVER AND BOYD LTD., EDINBURGH

STATISTICAL METHODS
FOR RESEARCH WORKERS

BY

RONALD A. FISHER, Sc.D., F.R.S.

ARTHUR BALFOUR PROFESSOR, UNIVERSITY OF CAMBRIDGE

The pioneer text-book for exact tests of significance, and analysis of Variance; fully illustrating a variety of computational procedures not available elsewhere.

Contents: Introductory. Diagrams. Distributions. Tests of Goodness of Fit, Independence and Homogeneity; with table of x^2. Tests of Significance of Means, Differences of Means, and Regression Coefficients. The Correlation Coefficient. Intra-class Correlations and the Analysis of Variance. Further Applications of the Analysis of Variance. The Principles of Statistical Estimation. Sources used from Data and Methods. Bibliography.

10th Edition.   Medium 8vo.   xvi+356 pp.   16s. net.

OLIVER AND BOYD LTD.
EDINBURGH AND LONDON

THIRD EDITION

STATISTICAL TABLES

FOR BIOLOGICAL, AGRICULTURAL AND MEDICAL RESEARCH

BY

RONALD A. FISHER, Sc.D., F.R.S.

ARTHUR BALFOUR PROFESSOR, UNIVERSITY OF CAMBRIDGE

AND

FRANK YATES, Sc.D.

HEAD OF STATISTICAL DEPARTMENT, ROTHAMSTED
EXPERIMENTAL STATION

Since the publication in 1925 of Fisher's "Statistical Methods for Research Workers," exact methods for the treatment of small samples, and the combination of experimental data, have come widely into use. In addition to the tables in that book, which have been, by permission, widely published in other statistical text-books, additional tables auxiliary to the treatment of special types of biological, medical and agricultural data, have since been computed, and are here brought together in a single volume.

Within its limited compass it is the aim of the authors to present a collection which shall be, by itself, sufficient to meet the greater part of the needs of the modern statistician.

3rd Revised Edition. Demy 4to. viii+112 pp. 16s. net.

OLIVER AND BOYD LTD.
EDINBURGH AND LONDON

IN PREPARATION

The Theory of Inbreeding

By RONALD A. FISHER, Sc.D., F.R.S.

In recent years considerable progress has been made with the theoretical problems arising out of the practice of inbreeding, while at the same time the immense economic success associated with this practice has begun to be realised by practical animal and plant breeders.

The use of inbreeding is, as has been realised for more than a hundred years, attended by grave dangers, and these can only be guarded against by clearly defined intentions in the inbreeding programme, and proper precautions that these intentions shall be carried out without the confusion of introducing other considerations, however important these may be by themselves.

Inbred stocks, while it is to be expected that they will be in themselves unprofitable, are of unique importance in animal and plant improvement by reason of the reliability of their breeding behaviour. From the point of view of pure research this makes them invaluable as a tool for precisely controlled progeny tests, while in agricultural development their value lies rather as the parent stocks of desirable crossbred (hybrid) combinations.

Demy 8vo.   **Approx. 140 pages.**

Regression Analysis of Production Costs and Factory Operations

By PHILIP LYLE

Shows how certain methods of statistical analysis, developed by statisticians primarily for the use of scientists and research workers, can be adapted for the solution of problems which rise in industry, thus providing from available data much useful information which cannot be extracted by the normal methods of accountancy.

The methods described have been in use in the sugar refining industry for some years for the analysis of production costs, labour, steam, and power consumption, etc. For the understanding of the book a knowledge of higher mathematics is not necessary.

Demy 8vo.   **With Tables and Diagrams.**   **15s. net.**

OLIVER AND BOYD

STATISTICAL METHODS IN RESEARCH AND PRODUCTION

WITH SPECIAL REFERENCE TO THE CHEMICAL INDUSTRY

Edited by

OWEN L. DAVIES, M.Sc., Ph.D.

" The book presents methods for dealing with the long tables of results or yields so often met with in large-scale production, on the basis of which the most economical working conditions must be chosen. The section on Specification will make an immediate appeal to those who had to produce during the war years hundreds of batches of material to comply with the exacting demands of the Chemical Inspectorate. This problem of specification is dealt with from the point of view of both producer and consumer, and a case is made out for statistical control as a substitute for rigid sample rules. A special section is devoted to the evergreen question of sampling. All the methods described in the book are clearly illustrated by examples selected from industrial chemical practice, and this adds reality to the very clear exposition. The authors are well aware of the necessity for eliminating extraneous variables before estimating degrees of correlation, while the use of frequency data to establish possible causes for accidents or mechanical failures is interesting.

" Throughout the work every attempt is made to lighten the mathematical tasks involved, and a spirited effort is made to transform what is often an unwieldy science into an easily handled tool."—*Times Review of Industry.*

Second Edition, revised. **304 pp.** **28s. net.**

PUBLISHED FOR

IMPERIAL CHEMICAL INDUSTRIES LIMITED

BY

OLIVER AND BOYD LTD.
EDINBURGH AND LONDON